Overcoming Weight Problems

The aim of the **Overcoming** series is to enable people with a range of common problems and disorders to take control of their own recovery program. Each title, with its specially tailored program, is devised by a practising clinician using the latest techniques of cognitive behavioral therapy – techniques which have been shown to be highly effective in changing the way patients think about themselves and their problems.

The series was initiated in 1993 by Peter Cooper, Professor of Psychology at Reading University and Research Fellow at the University of Cambridge in the UK whose original volume on overcoming bulimia nervosa and binge-eating continues to help many people in the USA, the UK and Europe.

Other titles in the series include:

All titles in the series are available by mail order.
Please see the order form at the back of this book.

OVERCOMING WEIGHT PROBLEMS

A self-help guide using Cognitive Behavioral Techniques

Jeremy Gauntlett-Gilbert
and Clare Grace

ROBINSON
London

Constable & Robinson Ltd
3 The Lanchesters
162 Fulham Palace Road
London W6 9ER
www.constablerobinson.com

First published in the UK by Robinson,
an imprint of Constable & Robinson Ltd 2005

A copy of the British Library Cataloguing in
Publication Data is available from the British Library.

ISBN 1- 84529-068-2

1 3 5 7 9 10 8 6 4 2

Important Note
This book is not intended to be substitute for medical advice or treatment.
Any person with a condition requiring medical attention should consult
a qualified medical practitioner or suitable therapist.

Printed and bound in the EU

Contents

Foreword

Why Cognitive Behavioral Therapy?

You may have picked up this book uncertain as to why a psychological therapy such as cognitive behavioral therapy could help you overcome your weight problems. Weight problems are physical problems, you might think. Cognitive behavioral therapy is for people who have psychological problems, and that's not me. In fact although CBT was developed initially for the treatment of depression, the techniques this therapy uses have been found to be extremely effective for a wide range of problems including compulsive gambling and drug and alcohol addiction. So what is CBT and how does it work?

In the 1950s and 1960s a set of techniques was developed, broadly collectively termed "behaviour therapy". These techniques shared two basic features. First, they aimed to remove symptoms (such as anxiety) by dealing with those symptoms themselves, rather than their deep-seated underlying historical causes (traditionally the focus of psychoanalysis, the approach developed by Sigmund Freud and his followers). Second, they were techniques, loosely related to what laboratory psychologists were finding out about the mechanisms of learning, which could potentially be put to the test, or had already been proven to be of practical value to sufferers. The area where these techniques proved of most value was in the treatment of anxiety disorders, especially specific phobias (such as fear of animals or heights) and agoraphobia, both notoriously difficult to treat using conventional psychotherapies.

After an initial flush of enthusiasm, discontent with behaviour therapy grew. There were a number of reasons for this, an important one of which was the fact that it did not deal with the internal thoughts which were so obviously central to the distress that patients were experiencing. In particular, behaviour therapy proved inadequate when it came to the treatment of depression. In the late 1960s and early 1970s a treatment was developed specifically for depression called "cognitive therapy". The pioneer in this enterprise was an American psychiatrist, Professor Aaron T. Beck, who developed a theory of depression which emphasized the importance of people's depressed styles of thinking. He also specified a new form of therapy. It would not be an exaggeration to say that Beck's work has changed the nature of psychotherapy, not just for depression but for a range of psychological problems.

The techniques introduced by Beck have been merged with the techniques developed earlier by the behaviour therapists to produce a therapeutic approach which has come to be known as "cognitive behavioral therapy". This therapy has been subjected to the strictest scientific testing and it has been found to be a highly successful treatment for a significant proportion of cases of depression. However it has become clear that specific patterns of thinking are associated with a range of psychological problems and that treatments which deal with these styles of thinking are highly effective. So effective cognitive behavioral treatments have been developed for anxiety disorders, like panic disorder, generalized anxiety disorder, specific phobias and social phobia, obsessive compulsive disorders and hypochondriasis (health anxiety), as well as for other conditions such as compulsive gambling, alcohol and drug addiction, and eating disorders like bulimia nervosa and binge-eating disorder. Indeed, cognitive behavioral techniques have a wide application beyond the narrow categories of psychological disorders: they have been applied effectively, for example, to helping people with low self-esteem, those with marital difficulties or weight problems, and those who wish to give up smoking.

The starting-point for CBT is that the way we think, feel and behave are all intimately linked, and changing the way we think about ourselves, our experiences and the world around us changes the way we feel and what we are able to do. So, by helping a depressed person identify and challenge their automatic depressive thoughts, a route out of a cycle of depressive thoughts and feelings can be found. Similarly, habitual responses, such as those associated with weight problems, are driven by a nexus of thoughts, feelings and behaviour; and CBT, as you will discover from this book, by providing a means for the behaviour to be brought under cognitive control, enables these responses to be undermined and a different kind of life to be possible.

Although effective CBT treatments have been developed for a wide range of problems, they are not widely available, and when people try to help themselves they often make matters worse. In recent years the community of cognitive behavioral therapists has responded to this situation. What they have done is to take the principles and techniques of specific cognitive behavioral therapies for particular problems and present them in self-help manuals. These manuals specify a systematic programme of treatment which the individual sufferer is advised to work through to overcome their difficulties. In this way, cognitive behavioral therapeutic techniques of proven value are being made available on the widest possible basis.

Self-help manuals are never going to replace therapists. Many people will need individual treatment from a qualified therapist. It is also the case that, despite the widespread success of cognitive behavioral therapy, some people will not respond to it and will need one of the other treatments available. Nevertheless, although research on the use of cognitive behavioral self-help manuals is at an early stage, the work done to date indicates that for a very great many people such a manual will prove sufficient for them to overcome their problems without professional help.

Foreword

Many people suffer silently and secretly for years. Sometimes appropriate help is not forthcoming, despite their efforts to find it. Sometimes they feel too ashamed or guilty to reveal their problems to anyone. For many of these people the cognitive behavioral self-help manual will provide a lifeline to recovery and a better future.

Professor Peter Cooper
The University of Reading, 2004

Introduction

Many people are passionate about losing weight, either for the sake of their health or for some other important personal reason.
Many of the same people really don't want to go on another quick-fix "diet".

Interesting statements, aren't they? It's true that most overweight people have taken steps to try to reduce their weight. They have very sensibly looked around them and seen what most people recommend as the best way to do it: "Go on a diet."

It is fair to say that lots of people are currently on diets! Across the world there must be millions of people who are trying to lose weight this way. An incredible amount of energy is being put into this, and many people have not stopped at dieting but have followed exercise programmes and group weight-loss programmes, attended private clinics and taken food supplements or replacements or, in the worst cases, unlicensed "weight-loss" pills. People have followed diets promising that particular foods are the "magic cure", or even that foods are good or bad in particular combinations.

Is it working? Well, around 250 million people across the world have serious weight problems, so perhaps most of these "cures" have not been a great success. Some quick-fix "diets" do work for some people in the short term. We have heard stories of people who have lost 20 or 30 stones through dieting. However, as soon as the diet is "broken", the weight goes back on. As NHS clinicians, we have seen people who have been overweight for years, and very often for decades. They have usually been through the horrible "yo-yo" pattern of regularly losing weight and putting it all (or more) back on again, and they often feel hopeless about the situation.

Many people have had such bad experiences with "dieting" that they blame themselves. They think that they must be particularly lazy or weak-willed to have such a problem with their weight. Or perhaps they decide that they must have particular psychological problems with food. We think that someone who has spent 10 years struggling with diets is very far from lazy! Unfortunately, there are some health professionals who think that overweight people just need to "pull their socks up" and stop being so greedy. Very often they are simply told to "eat less and exercise more". This is like a business consultant telling an ailing company, "Well, you just need to sell more of your products. Then you'll make more money." The advice is correct, of course, but without any details of *how you would do that*, it is useless.

However, it is not all bad news. People do succeed at losing weight. We have seen people lose huge amounts of weight – 11 stones, for example – through only simple changes to their food intake and exercise. There is also the huge satisfaction of seeing people lose weight quite gradually – perhaps only a pound or two in a week – but being pretty sure that the weight will stay off. For someone who has spent 10 years losing weight through diets and then putting it back on, permanent weight loss – even if it is slow – is a huge achievement. And people *can* do it, even if they have been trying for years. We know this from our clinical experience and from scientific studies (more about this later).

We wrote this book because we believe passionately that many weight problems can be helped. We are a clinical psychologist and a dietician. Whilst we cannot give you all of our professional training, we will try to pass on some of our skills and knowledge, including all of the "top tips" – the most useful information on losing weight for the long term.

Introduction

Most problems are easier to deal with if they are well understood. So first we will look at three important questions:

1. Why are so many people overweight?
2. Why don't quick-fix "diets" work in the long term?
3. Is there an alternative?

Why Are So Many People Overweight?

Hundreds of thousands of people are overweight and the number of people who are seriously overweight ("obese" in technical language) has *trebled* in the last 20 years in the UK. This pattern has been seen in most countries throughout the world, particularly in USA. It is estimated that 300,000 Americans died from diseases related to weight problems in 2001. Doctors in the USA are worried that more people are dying from being overweight than from smoking. It is possible that, for the first time in a very long time, the current generation of young people will have shorter lives than their parents. Many more of these young people will be overweight, and they will suffer the associated health problems.

Why is this happening? Either there has suddenly been a big rise in "laziness" or "weakness of will" across the world (however unlikely!) or something has happened in society that is making it harder and harder to stay a healthy weight.

Moreover, there are still many negative attitudes towards people who are overweight. You may have experienced some of these. Overweight people are seen as unattractive and stupid. It is still seen as OK to make jokes about fat people on the TV or in newspapers. There is good evidence from the USA that overweight students are less likely to be accepted into good colleges, no matter what their grades. Overweight executives make less money. Overweight people are often abused on the street.

It is an odd situation – we live in a society that seems to be making people fat, but that also punishes overweight people. On the other hand slimness is portrayed as necessary for success and happiness. Almost every magazine, newspaper and shop window includes pictures of very thin women (there are thin – or muscled – men as well, but women are much more affected) and there is a public obsession with which celebrities have lost – or put on – weight.

The fashion industry does worse than this, however. It sometimes tries to sell a body image that is impossible to achieve for the vast majority of the population. We have colleagues who work with people with anorexia. Health clinics are seeing more and more of these people. There are also more anorexic people hanging on at lower and lower weights. Anorexia is more likely to result in death than any other psychiatric disorder. Yet some fashion models clearly have a weight that is in the anorexic range. And they are meant to be a good example of beauty.

You may think that we are exaggerating. However, we are very serious. Have a look at the dummies used to hang women's clothes in shop windows. A study in the *British Medical Journal* showed that if these shop dummies were real women, they would be so dangerously thin that they would no longer be able to menstruate. Yet these are supposed to be the "ideal shape" for a woman.

How has it got this bad?

It's not clear why we have come to admire body shapes that are so thin as to be unhealthy. However, it is a little easier to work out why so many more people have weight problems these days. The answer is that the environment has changed in two ways:

- We are encouraged to eat more than we need.
- It is becoming easier and easier to be inactive.

"Portion distortion"
So, how has it become easier to eat more? Portion sizes are changing, something called "portion distortion". Standard packets of food are becoming bigger and the average size of a meal is getting larger in many restaurants. The size of a portion

of chips in fast-food restaurants is quietly getting bigger and bigger. Food manufacturers know that people like a bargain. If a person sees "50% extra free", or "buy one get one free", they are likely to think that they have saved money.

The dangerous thing about "portion distortion" is that we *might not change our eating habits at all*, but the amount that we eat would still go up. Here is an example of how dangerous this effect can be:

- In the 1980s the average packet of crisps weighed 25g. These days, almost all packets of crisps weigh 40g.
- Imagine a person who eats five packets of crisps a week . . .
- If they eat *five* of the 40g bags, that is the same as eating *eight* of the old 25g packets.
- So switching to the 40g bags is like eating three extra bags per week.
- Or 12 bags per month.
- Or 150 bags extra per year!
- Over five years, this person would eat *an extra 19 kg of crisps* (*that's 3 stones!*) without changing their eating habits at all.

Of course, it is not just crisps. If you look around you, "portion distortion" is everywhere. A coffee-shop "cookie" was once the size of a biscuit – these days it is likely to be the size of a small plate.

Portion distortion is only part of the story. If you take a trip through any Western city, it is amazing to see how many shops sell fast food, fried food and takeaways. Think of the number of "eat all you like" buffets, extra huge pizzas, free offers. It is also obvious that these days there are many more exciting – and fattening – foods to enjoy. Think of the new ranges of ice-cream flavours or deep-fried crisps on offer. They taste marvellous! Unfortunately, it can be difficult to enjoy them in moderation . . .

So we are definitely being tempted to eat more. This would be less of a problem if we were very fit, active people – we would just burn it off. But . . .

We are spending less time being active

Again, it's not the case that we have suddenly become lazy. It is just becoming easier and easier to sit still for most of our lives. Some of you may remember an episode of the American sitcom *Friends* in which two of the characters buy huge leather chairs and spend their entire days watching TV. They only stop to ring up (from their mobile phones) and have pizza delivered to the door. Of course, this is comedy – but like all good comedy it has a bit of truth to it.

Many of the parts of modern life that make us sit still are great. Playstations, videos and DVDs are often fantastic entertainment. We can do such an amazing number of things with a home computer. Mobile phones are incredibly useful and save lots of time. Where would we be without our cars and TV? But the result is less activity.

So here is the picture: we live in an environment that tends to make it difficult for people to control their weight by persuading them to eat more and be less active. The same society promotes thinness as a requirement for happiness and success. So it offers overweight people the traditional "diet".

Why Quick-Fix "Diets" Are Not the Way Forward

Of course, the first thing to be said about quick-fix "diets" is that they often work very well – for a while. People who go on them often manage to lose a few pounds, and sometimes even more. If we only needed to "diet" so that we could look good in a swimming costume for our summer holidays, then traditional "diets" might be fine.

Yet what so many people in our society need is to understand how to keep weight off for the long term. In order to do this, we need to find an eating and exercise plan that we can imagine doing for the rest of our lives. Who can imagine following some of the quick-fix "diets" for the rest of their lives? This is the problem – and here are some reasons why.

Introduction

They are not very flexible or interesting

"Diets" can become boring. It helps that they are often simple and easy to follow – you just have to eat what you are told. However, we were not designed to eat the same things every day. And routines like this may not fit into our lives. Most people go out for dinner once in a while, or have a takeaway. How does this fit into a very strict "diet"? And how many of us would be willing to give up going out for dinner *forever*, so that we could stick to our diet?

They tell us to stop eating certain foods

Most of us know that as soon as we are told that we "can't" eat something, we begin to crave it and thoughts of it will pop into our heads all of the time. Needless to say, this is not going to work well for weight loss. How many people would be willing to spend the rest of their lives without eating chocolate (or potato chips or cheese)? Any diet that "bans" foods will be very difficult to follow in the long term.

They can be quite "extreme" solutions

Some diets ask us to make quite drastic changes to our eating habits. Some ask us to replace meals with a supplement and others suggest cutting back on food intake quite severely. These approaches can suit some people, particularly if they have suffered from weight problems for a very long time and have tried lots of different "solutions" without success. After all of this effort, they may be quite pleased to try an "extreme" diet. And really drastic diets *can* result in very rapid weight loss. The real challenge is in keeping this weight off. At some point, the "extreme" diet has to stop and we will be tempted to go back to our old habits – and then what will happen?

They are designed to be short term

This is the basic problem with most quick-fix "diets". Most of them sell the idea that you can do something *for a short period of time*, and then your weight problem will be fixed *forever*. This will not happen. Everyone knows that as soon as a person stops a diet, they go back to the same old habits of eating and activity that they had before. Unfortunately, these were the habits that made them overweight in the first place.

Magazines and TV are addicted to short-term solutions. Even when they are trying to sound sophisticated, they get it wrong. Here is a headline from a recent magazine: "We all know that diets don't work. Try our new 28-day plan . . ."

This promise of a short-term "fix" can be seen in many areas of life. For example, many people these days have money problems and there are lots of adverts that say something like: "Take out a big loan from us – you can pay off your credit cards and all of your other debts at once." Of course, this is true. But if the person who takes the loan does not fix the basic problem – that they are spending more than they earn – then no short-term "fix" will help them. It's just the same for eating – if a person does not change their basic habits of eating and activity, then no diet will help. This leads us to another problem with quick-fix "diets".

They ignore exercise – or don't treat it as very important

Most approaches to weight loss focus only on food. Have a look in your local bookshop at the section that has the "diet" books. Now compare the number that are about food to the number that talk about exercise as well. Most only focus on food. This is a problem. Lots of recent scientific research shows that exercise is very important in preventing weight gain in the first place and in helping people keeping weight off over the longer term. So if we are thinking about weight loss for the long term, we cannot ignore activity.

They are based on a "fad" theory of how to lose weight

There are so many "diets" that claim to have found the magical cure to permanent weight loss. "If you just follow this special formula, your weight will disappear quickly and easily". It would be wonderful if this were true. However, these "diets" often have no good-quality scientific evidence to support their claims. It is better to put your time and effort into approaches more likely to be of help to you.

Of course, some people will lose weight by using the "magical" approaches – however, this will have something to do with the overall change to their diet and nothing at all to do with the "fad" theory behind it.

One thing about dieting is essential

There is a bottom line here. What is needed is nothing more – and nothing less – than to eat a balanced, healthy diet and to burn off at least as much energy through activity as you take in through food. There is not a shred of scientific evidence for any approach that promises that you can somehow do better than this. If there were, we promise that we would tell you – and we would be doing it ourselves!

Most quick-fix diets are unhelpful for most people

We have listed plenty of reasons why quick-fix "diets" are not the way forward. There are some exceptions to the rules above. For example, some systems are quite flexible and do not make you "ban" any foods. However, on the whole, the diet industry continues to sell solutions that have all of the problems above – and they are making millions doing it.

We hope to show you a good alternative to all of these problems. Before this, though, there is one final problem with diets – yes, another one!

The "Perfect Diet"

Imagine that we have invented the Perfect Diet. It is flexible, does not ban any foods, is healthy, allows for the occasional treat and will result in steady weight loss. We have made this diet scientifically perfect for you. We know that if you stay with it, you will lose weight.

Imagine that we give you this diet plan, but there are some things that we cannot give you. Imagine that *nothing else in your life changes*. That means you are still:

- the same person
- with the same routine
- the same family and friends
- the same emotions and attitudes

How well would you do?

Here are some things that might happen:

- Old habits of snacking or bingeing might start again – sometimes with you hardly noticing them.
- Other people could get in the way – either by actively trying to stop you losing weight or by just refusing to be helpful with the weight-loss programme.
- Other parts of your life may get in the way – for example, having to have crisps in for the kids or not really having a safe area to go out walking in.
- You might not really have good personal reasons to lose weight but be trying the Perfect Diet because you felt you "ought" to or because the doctor said so.
- You might not really be serious about weight loss – you might go through the motions but not really plan or expect to succeed.
- You might not believe that the Perfect Diet – or any new programme – will work.
- You might not believe, deep down, that you can stick to any programme and make it work.
- You might have worries that the programme will fail and you will put on even more weight.
- You might quite enjoying the indulgence and pleasure of breaking the diet.

- You might feel that you shouldn't have to do this, that it isn't fair.
- You might break the diet just a little then say, "I've blown it now," and lose track for days.

Most of us would have problems with some of these, even if we were using the Perfect Diet. Why is this?

The difficulty is that eating and activity happen in our lives – and our lives are often very complicated. It's all very well having the perfect plan, but how can it succeed if our lives are going to get in the way?

All of the changes that we have to make to lose weight have to be put into practice in the context of our own unique lives and our own unique set of beliefs and emotions. This might not sound easy. However, we know that people can do it. It is worth finding out about these successes.

Weight-Loss "Experts"

American scientists have been studying a group of over 700 "experts" at weight loss. This group is called the National Weight Control Registry (NWCR). Here's why we call them "experts":

- On average, people in this group have lost nearly 5 stones (30 kg) in weight and have kept it off for more than five years. These are remarkable results, far better than those achieved by the best available weight-loss programmes.
- There is also very good news about how weight loss has affected these individuals' lives. On average, the NWCR group's mood and self-confidence have improved and they have increased levels of energy and mobility.
- The results are particularly impressive as most of the group had attempted to lose weight many times in the past. They had lost (and presumably regained) large amounts of weight before they managed to keep it off.

Clearly, the NWCR group managed to do what thousands of people across the world would love to do. It is worth spending some time looking at how they did it.

First of all, most of these people had good reasons to lose weight. Over three-quarters of the sample said that some event made them decide to lose weight. This was usually something medical (like back pain or fatigue), or some important emotional event (for example, a relationship breaking down due to weight).

Then the NWCR group changed *both* their eating *and* their exercise habits. The most common changes were that they:

- ate regularly – on average five times per day
- ate breakfast
- changed certain types or classes of foods
- changed portion sizes
- focused on reducing fat

The "experts" also got very serious about activity. However, the types of exercise were just as simple as the changes to their eating. Most chose one or two activities such as walking, swimming, cycling or the gym. However, it's worth pointing out that the NWCR group did quite a lot of exercise and burned a large amount of energy this way.

What the "experts" tell us

The studies of the NWCR group do not give us any magical new ideas about methods of weight loss. However, we think that there are some very significant lessons to be learned from them.

First, it is never too late to try to lose weight. Most of the NWCR group were dieting "veterans" who had lost and regained a good deal of weight in the past.

Second, the NWCR group were generally happier when they had lost weight. Many people worry that they will have to permanently "starve" themselves to keep weight off and that they might be slim but they would be miserable. This doesn't seem to be the case in the NWCR. Higher levels confidence and happiness were reported after weight loss.

Third, and perhaps most importantly, the NWCR group shows that *changing habits* is the key. What they did was simple, but they managed to keep it going year after year.

So what does "changing habits" mean?

Most of our lives are made up of habits. When we get up in the morning, our habits start. We either get straight out of bed or groan and hit the "snooze" button. That's a habit. When we get up, some people put on a dressing gown, some don't. That's a habit too.

Our habits are so routine we usually don't even think about them. But they can be important. Some people are in the habit of having a fried breakfast, some have cereal and some have nothing. These habits will certainly affect those people's weight in the long term.

Here are some important facts about habits:

- When you are used to a habit, it doesn't seem like a big effort.
- However, changing a habit is difficult and needs some effort and concentration.
- After a while, though, it begins to seem like less of an effort. That is because a *new* habit has been formed.

In terms of weight loss, this means that there is good and bad news. First, it will be difficult at the beginning. You will be trying to make new habits and break old ones. This is going to be hard, as anyone who has stopped biting their nails or quit smoking can tell you. However, when the new habit is in place, it will become easier.

There is evidence from the NWCR study to back up this idea. As we know, most people with weight problems find that it is relatively easy to lose weight but really hard to keep that weight off. The NWCR group found the opposite.

Three-quarters of them found that keeping weight off was easier, or equally easy, than losing the weight. Changing their habits was the hard part; once this was done, the new habits just kept themselves going – and the weight kept off!

The Goals of This Book and How to Achieve Them

You may be curious to know how you can do it too. In this book we will show you how to:

- change your habits of activity and eating over the long term
- have a flexible approach to activity and eating that is healthy and balanced
- make all of these changes happen in your own unique life
- manage all of this yourself, without having to rely on someone else's ideas or support

We are going to introduce you to some of the latest ideas on how to change behaviour. We know they work. They all come under the heading of "cognitive behavioral therapy," or CBT.

What is cognitive behavioral therapy?

"Cognitive behavioral therapy" is a long-winded term – one patient once commented, "What? Carpet bagel therapy?!" – but the phrase is usually shortened to "CBT" and the overall idea is not hard to explain.

CBT is a form of psychological therapy. Now you may be thinking, "I need help with my eating, not a shrink!" But CBT is really useful for weight loss. It was originally developed for the treatment of depression, but it has been shown to be a highly effective way of treating lots of different emotional and behavioural problems.

The idea behind CBT is that behaviour is always very closely connected to our thoughts and feelings. So if a person wants to change their habits effectively, they will probably have to change their attitudes and deal with some emotions differently. For example:

A *thought*: "This is hopeless. I'll never lose this weight. There's just no point trying"
    might be related to . . .
A *feeling*: Feeling miserable, sad, low
    which might be related to . . .
A *physical reaction*: Feeling completely out of energy and craving sweets
    which might be related to . . .
A form of *behaviour*: Staying in, not going out, "comfort eating" with sweets
    which might be related to . . .
Everything else *all over again*.

If you understand how all of these things happen, you can begin to change the patterns. CBT shows you the best ways to do this.
    There are particular parts of CBT that are important:

- It focuses on feelings, thoughts and behaviour *in the here and now* – not in childhood, for example.
- It is a *teaching* approach – it does not aim to "fix" people by telling them what to do but by teaching them the skills to "fix" themselves.
- It is an active approach that focuses on trying things out. The trick is to experiment and see what works.

All of this will become clearer as we go through the book.

How to Use This Book

What this book is about

This book is about losing weight in a healthy way over the long term permanently in order to keep as healthy as possible and have the best possible quality of life. It is not primarily about losing weight to look good. We think that it is important not to support the idea that everybody should be a "perfect" shape. Many people spend lots of time worrying about their weight when they are perfectly healthy. Of course, there's *absolutely nothing wrong* with wanting to look good and the techniques in this book will work just fine to achieve this. But the main aim is health and a good quality of life.

This book is about changing eating *and activity*. They go together. For someone who is serious about losing weight in the long term, neither is optional.

What this book is not *about*

This book is not about curing eating disorders. Eating disorders (bulimia, anorexia, binge-eating disorder) can be dreadful problems that seriously interfere with people's lives. There are good books, support services and health services for people with these problems. A good place to start might be some of the other books in this series, for example *Bulimia Nervosa and Binge Eating* by Peter Cooper or *Overcoming Anorexia* by Christopher Freeman.

- If you are bingeing and then vomiting or using laxatives regularly – for example, every week – please go to your doctor. (Many overweight people have vomited once or twice in their lives in order to lose weight, but this doesn't mean that they are bulimic. It is time to be concerned if you are *still* doing it *regularly*.)
- If your BMI is below 20 (*see below*) then this book is not for you. Losing even more weight will hurt you. It will not make you happier. There are people who have the skills and knowledge to help you with this difficulty. Please use the services that are available to you – ask your doctor.

How this book is organized

We have written this book to a very clear plan, but we realize that people will read it in different ways. Some people might prefer to read the sections that seem most useful and skip the rest. Others will start at page 1 and read slowly and thoroughly to the end. There is no right or wrong way to do it. However, we wrote the book in a particular way, and it is useful for you to know why.

The book is written in two stages:

Part One – Chapters 1, 2 and 3 – provides the foundations. It aims to get you motivated, to remove mental blocks and to help you understand your habits. These are hugely useful skills that can be used in all sorts of situations.

Chapter 1 shows you how to work out your motivation and has ideas about what is bad for motivation – for example, guilt.

However, even if a person has motivation, they still might not believe that they are really capable of losing weight. So it is important to deal with thoughts and beliefs about weight loss (Chapter 2). Some patterns of thinking can undermine our motivation and confidence.

Finally, before a person can get started with real change, they have to understand their own habits of eating and exercise. This is covered in Chapter 3.

Part Two – Chapters 4 to 9 – is about how to make the changes in your life.

Chapters 4 and 5 explain sensible ways to get activity into your life and to eat healthily and well for the long term.

However, knowing how to do something is not the same as being able to do it. Chapter 6 covers the hard work of changing your routines and habits.

When you make some changes, difficult emotions (for example sadness) or physical feelings (hunger or cravings) may come up. Chapter 7 covers how to deal with these.

Other people may also not be very helpful with the process of weight loss. Chapter 8 covers how to deal with partners, friends and others.

Finally, Chapter 9 sums everything up and shows you how to plan for the future.

Before you start, work out how overweight you are

A good start is learn how professionals calculate health risks due to being overweight. They use a particular measure known as body mass index, or BMI. BMI is just a measure of weight that takes account of height. Obviously, a taller person will weigh more, but will not necessarily be fatter. You can calculate your own BMI using the table in Appendix I (*page 233*).

So, what does this number mean? Here are the classifications that professionals use:

19.9 or less	Underweight	Should not be losing weight
20–24.9	Healthy weight	Should keep weight stable
25–29.9	Overweight	Health at risk from weight
30–39.9	Obese	Health at high risk from weight
40+	Morbidly obese	Health at very high risk, weight loss is a priority

Remember your BMI and write it down. We will refer to it again later.

You will need equipment

You will need to have somewhere where you can write things down. Many people use a notebook. Others have a file, or a place where they store pieces of notepaper. If you use a computer regularly, or a personal digital assistant (PDA), these can be a great choice as well. You need to be able to express yourself honestly, so make sure whatever method you choose is confidential if you need it to be.

Summary

- Many sensible people have tried to lose weight for years by using quick-fix solutions.

- These usually haven't worked and sometimes have left them feeling as if they had no willpower or were lazy.
- However, being overweight is a problem affecting more and more people in our society.
- Modern life tempts us to eat too much tasty food and keeps us inactive.
- Quick-fix diets are not the way forward for most people: they are rigid, short-term and often rely on a "fad" theory of weight loss.
- However, people *can* lose weight and keep it off – and it is never too late to try.
- The solution is changing habits of eating and exercise for the long term.

PART ONE

Fundamentals

Motivation to Change

"You've got to be motivated if you want to lose weight!"
"Dieting takes willpower, you know!"

There's a lot of talk about "willpower" when it comes to dieting
and exercise. Most of it can end up making people feel bad about
themselves. If a person has tried to diet many times but always
regained the weight, they often end up thinking that they must
have no "willpower" or be really lazy.

In our view, this is crazy. How can you call someone who has
tried a dozen different diets "lazy"? Also, there are reasons to be
suspicious about people who talk about "willpower" a lot. They
very often seem to act as if they were in the army, and have a
rather extreme approach to dieting and exercise. This
approach may suit them, but it will not be much use for most
of us.

It is true that people have often lost their commitment to
weight loss. Not everyone is pleased by the thought of another
attempt at losing weight. Some people make a half-effort – that
is, they have a go at a diet but leave out the bits that they don't
like. Others drift on and off of diets – they try anything for a few
days, but get bored quickly. Anger is quite common. Many
people have had such a miserable time with dieting that they are
furious with the whole diet industry (quite rightly) and with the
professionals who try to persuade them to lose weight. There is
also the amazing human ability not to think about difficult

things. If something can make you unhappy, it is a lot easier to push it to the back of your mind.

These are all understandable reactions to the process of dieting. In fact, they are all normal reactions to situations that involve failure and difficulty.

Ignore "willpower" and think about motivation

The good news is that psychologists think that the term "willpower" is pretty meaningless. It's obvious that people have "willpower" and "motivation" for some things and not for others. For example, a teenager may be putting little effort into studying for exams. They may avoid doing the work or do so little that is makes no difference. They might find excuses for why they are not studying, or complain when they are forced to. However, the same teenager might have a huge passion for football. They might practise in cold wind and driving rain night after night. They might have an incredible knowledge of players and clubs. Does this mean that they have willpower or not? The answer is yes when they are working towards something that matters to them personally. Otherwise, no.

That difference is the focus of this chapter. Experience tells us that if people try to lose weight for important personal reasons, they tend to do well. If they try because they think they "should", or try half-heartedly, they don't do well at all.

There are ways to discover, or perhaps rediscover, your important personal reasons to lose weight. Even if you think you are a pretty motivated person, or that you have obvious reasons to lose weight, read on. All of us can learn something from the exercises in this chapter.

What is Motivation?

Talking about "motivation" can be a bit unclear. Different people use the word to mean different things. In order to be completely clear about what we are talking about, here are some descriptions of a motivated person and a not very motivated person:

A motivated person:

- knows their own personal reasons for doing something
- is not doing something because they "should" or "ought to"
- is doing something for themselves
- really wants to do something and is willing to make the effort
- is ready for a long-term effort
- knows that there are going to be difficulties and doesn't fool themselves about this
- knows the disadvantages of what they are going to do and has decided that they can live with them
- is willing to experience some unpleasant feelings to get to their goal
- knows that there is no guarantee of success
- is willing to work on their own – they might get advice and support, but they know that they must make the effort themselves.
- knows what they want, why they want it and why it is important to them

On the other hand, a not very motivated person:

- is doing something only because their doctor, or their friends, or their partner wants them to
- does not have good reasons to do it
- hopes someone will come and fix the problem for them
- just wants to follow a programme (if it goes wrong, they will blame the programme)
- just dips their toe in, rather than putting their heart into it
- thinks that a bit of excitement or energy ("Yeah! Let's do it!") is the same as real motivation
- expects things to work perfectly
- will not start something unless they are pretty sure they can succeed
- is willing to do anything as long as it's not difficult

We all recognize a bit of ourselves in the second list, particularly when it comes to doing something difficult. But there is some good news here – that doesn't matter at all! The trick is to build up positive reasons to make changes. If you have these, then the negatives won't be an issue.

What is motivation made of?

Now we know what motivation looks like, but that doesn't help us to be motivated ourselves. I can watch an Olympic gymnast on TV and recognize their moves, but that doesn't mean I can do what they do. In order to get real motivation we have to know what it is made up of. We need to understand what is going on in the mind of a motivated person.

In order to be motivated, to be committed and passionate about doing something, we need:

essential!!

1. To have important personal reasons for doing it.
2. To believe that it is possible to achieve it.

If either of these is missing there is no motivation. For example, imagine that I would love to be an Olympic gymnast. Imagine that this had been my dream for years and that it meant a lot to me personally. Unfortunately, even if this were true, I still wouldn't be motivated to start training. This is because I would not, deep down, believe it was possible for me to be an Olympic gymnast (and I'd be right – I can't even touch my toes). So I don't have the realistic belief that I can achieve my goal. And even with the best reasons in the world, I will not get motivated.

On the other hand, I am perfectly capable of cleaning out my shed, which has needed doing for months. It's obvious that I am able to do this, so I have got number 2 this time. The trouble is, I don't have very many good reasons to do it right now. There are lots of other things that are more important to me. This time, I don't have the important personal reasons. My shed is going to remain untidy for quite a long time.

So, in order to succeed at something people need both good reasons to do it and the belief that they can do it. In this section we will deal with the reasons. The belief will be covered in chapters 2 and 3. For now, the focus is on finding good personal reasons for weight loss.

Reasons for Losing Weight

You may be thinking that your reasons for losing weight are pretty obvious! You want to look better, be healthier, be more mobile. It can be no fun to live in a society where being overweight equals being unattractive, stupid and lazy. But we've had odd experiences with "obvious" reasons. A good example is the gentleman below, an intelligent man who had an excellent understanding of the health risks of being overweight:

> *"My family has a history of diabetes. I know that I need to lose weight – I've seen what diabetes can do to people. If you don't control it properly, you can end up going blind or having your limbs amputated! I know all of this stuff, but it doesn't seem to make me want to lose weight. It just doesn't make any difference when I've got the food in front of me."*

Most people would agree that the risk of losing an arm or a leg would motivate them to take action. Unfortunately, it does not always work like this. Not all reasons give a person real emotional energy, even if they seem important. It's useful to remember the NWCR study here. The people who lost lots of weight and kept it off generally had a health scare or something that really shocked them – and those reasons gave them the energy to succeed.

In order to get the kind of mental and emotional energy and commitment that's needed, we are going to step away from weight loss for a moment. Weight loss is a difficult task. But we have all done difficult things in our lives. How did we achieve them?

What reasons can motivate you to do things that are difficult?

Everyone has overcome difficulties at some point in their lives or made a serious effort at something that they didn't have to do. It's helpful to remember and analyse these times. Whatever gave you the strength then may also give you the strength for weight loss. Try to remember some times when you have done the following:

- done something difficult that you didn't have to do
- experienced difficulties and kept going
- decided to do something that mattered to you, even though you weren't certain you would succeed
- kept on doing something difficult for a really long time
- been really determined and focused
- been seen by others to have been really determined or focused

When you have remembered a time like this, try to work out what gave you the energy and kept you going. For many people it was some kind of standard, or ideal, such as "being a good parent" or "seeing things through", while for others it was working towards some important goal that they could see "in the distance". For example:

- "I was determined always to have time for my children, no matter how tired or rushed I was. It's really important for me to be a good parent."
- "I've always worked hard at my job and always will. I enjoy doing my work to the best of my ability and delivering a really great service. I love to see customers delighted with what I can give them."
- "I kept phoning my friend Paula, as she was going through a rough divorce. It was hard to listen to her at times, but I was determined to be a friend who was there when I was needed."

- "I worked hard to get that extra qualification. I was determined to keep developing my own skills and interests. I am the kind of person who keeps learning and I always see things through."
- "I'll do any work I have to in order to travel. I scrimped and saved for months to get the money together. You only get one life and there's a huge beautiful world out there. I'm not going to miss it!"

The point of this exercise is to be clear about the things that really matter to you. The name that we give these things really doesn't matter – they could be called "values" or "passions" or "principles", but we have decided to use "reasons". We may think that we know what our reasons are, but it is wise to look back to see what has really motivated us in the past. It might not be the same.

Of course, people change. So just focusing on what has worked in the past will not do the job completely. People's lives change too and something can become important that has never been as issue before. For example, some people think that it is important to look after their elderly parents, but their parents have previously been healthy, so the issue has not come up before.

It can be hard to work out what your reasons are, particularly if you have not thought about things in this way before. Sometimes it is not clear what is a reason and what isn't. It is also quite easy to get completely stuck and not come up with anything. Other people just come up with what sound like the "right" answers, such as "my family". So here are some ideas and exercises to help out.

Helpful ways to think about reasons

Thinking about what's important to you is a huge topic, so it's helpful to think about particular areas of your life one at a time. Here are some areas to think about. It is useful to think what matters to you under each heading. Also, work out *how much* each reason that you think of matters to you. Is it something that you would barely get out of bed for? Or would you move heaven and earth to achieve it?

This isn't a complete list, of course. If there are other things that matter to you that are not on this list, then just add them. Conversely, some of these categories may not apply to you.

- Relationships – your partnerships, in the present or future
- Family – your children, siblings, parents
- Social life – what kind of friend you want to be, how you want your friendships to develop?
- Work – your career or vocation, your ambitions
- Education and training – how do you want to develop your mind and skills?
- Recreation – how do you want to spend your leisure time? What's your idea of fun and relaxation?
- Spirituality – however you relate to the meaning of your life, the bigger picture
- Citizenship – your role in society, perhaps "giving something back"
- Health and well-being – how do you want to maintain your health, for example sleep, exercise, smoking?

When you're doing this, try to be honest. Don't just write what sounds good if that doesn't really feature in your most important priorities. No one else need ever read this list.

Here are some ways to generate more ideas:

- Think of people whose lives or characters you admire.
- Remember the things that you used to dream about as a child.
- Imagine yourself as you would like to be. What does this person want out of life? What do they value?
- Imagine you are at your own funeral, hearing people talk about your life. What would you like to hear them saying?
- Find someone who's known you a long time and ask them what they think are your real passions and values.

Once you have some ideas, write them down. Put everything down, even if it doesn't seem as though it's very helpful for weight loss. It's important to be honest.

Put your reasons in positive terms

The actual words that you use when writing down your reasons are important. Reasons are most useful when they are put in positive terms. For example, these are two different ways of seeing the same situation:

> *"I worked two jobs at the same time because we had so little money. It was really hand to mouth – I just had to keep going to pay the bills. I don't know where I found the strength."*
>
> *"I worked two jobs at the same time because we had so little money. I was determined to do what I had to in order to keep family life normal. I made sure that the kids didn't want for anything and I didn't want to have to disrupt their lives by having to move to a smaller place. I found the strength because I was doing it for them."*

The second way is just as true, but puts things in a more positive light. It focuses on what was really important in that situation. In the first example, it may seem that paying bills was the important thing. But that only mattered because unpaid bills would have disrupted family life. Family life was what was really important, so when the person in this example comes to write their reasons down, they should focus on that. It is true, and it is also more helpful for the future, when the going may get tough with weight loss. This leads us on to the next question.

How does weight loss connect to the things that you value?

The answer to this question may be clear already. Alternatively, there may seem to be no connections at all between what's important to you and weight loss. The next exercise is an imaginative yet very practical way of joining the two up.

The "Five Years" Exercise

This is the single most powerful exercise that you can do for your motivation. It is hard for most of us to get the motivation *now* for things that will benefit us *in the future*. However, this is exactly what needs to happen if weight loss is going to be successful in the long term. So the "Five Years" exercise uses your imagination to picture what your life in the future will be and how your weight will affect that.

Take this exercise seriously and give it plenty of time. Do it when you have as much time and peace and quiet as you can get – it will not be as effective if you do it on the back of an envelope or in a hurry. It involves using your imagination for a while, so find the best time and place for this. It really needs to be done all at once – you can't do part of it and come back to it, though you may find that you can add to it as you think of new things or find out new information. In fact, doing the "Five Years" may become a new habit!

You will need somewhere to write things down as you think of them.

Imagine yourself in five years' time

This may sound a little hard, but you can do it. Imagine two different futures and do them one at a time.

1. *Weight-gain future*
In this future, you have lost no weight at all and have even gained some (most adults gain weight over a five-year period). If you are quite overweight, it may be that your back or joints have suffered by this point, so include this. Your health is the same as it is now, or perhaps slightly worse. You may have slightly less energy, more aches and pains, and be slightly less mobile.

In order to get this future clear in your head, ask yourself these questions:

- Where will you be living?
- What will you be doing with your time? What will you be able, or not able, to do?
- What will have happened by then? Pay attention to any big events that you know will come up in the next five years. What will these events have been like?
- Imagine your age in five years' time.
- Imagine the ages of other people close to you.
- Imagine a typical day – getting out of bed and so on. Imagine all of your sensations, including energy, tiredness and pain.
- How will you be feeling about yourself?
- Imagine how others will be feeling about you. Will they be pleased, or worried about you?

Try to imagine this future and make it as realistic as possible.

When you have got this in mind, you will find it easier to imagine the other possibility.

2. Weight-loss future

In the second future, you have lost a substantial amount of weight. (You have had five years to do it in!) Be realistic – don't imagine miracles. But you are fitter and more active. Your general health is better – that is, you sleep better and have more energy.

Again, ask yourself the same questions:

- Where will you be living?
- What will you be doing with your time? What will you be able, or not able, to do?
- What will have happened by then? Pay attention to any big events that you know will come up in the next five years. What will these events have been like?
- Imagine your age in five years' time.
- Imagine the age of other people close to you.

13

- Imagine a typical day – getting out of bed and so on. Imagine all of your sensations, including energy, tiredness and pain.
- How will you be feeling about yourself?
- Imagine how others will be feeling about you. Will they be pleased, or worried about you?

Include the positives and negatives

When you imagine your two different futures, don't forget to include both positives and negatives. For example, there may be good things about the weight-gain future. You may be delighted that you haven't had to think about weight loss! You may be pleased that you haven't wasted your time dieting. And in the weight-loss future, perhaps you have to go out and exercise in the evening when you don't feel like it, or when it's cold outside. The point is to be as imaginative as possible, to really try to imagine your two futures in as much detail as possible, and to be realistic.

In five years' time, will weight loss really matter to you?

What are the important differences between the two futures? Think about these differences in terms of the reasons that you wrote down above. If you can see that weight loss will affect the things that matter to you, then this will be the heart of your motivation. If not, things will be trickier. Again, write your reasons down, and put them in a positive way.

The "Five Years" exercise was important for **Jackie:**

"I'm 38 years old, and my son, Craig, is 10. The first thing that comes into my mind when I think about the next five years is my age! I will have had my fortieth birthday and I suppose I will be in my mid-forties. That's a funny thought. When it comes to health, I've always thought, somehow, that people in their forties need to be more careful than people in their thirties. It just sounds older. Craig will be 15. I can't imagine him that old, but I suppose by that time he will be wanting to spend a lot less time with me. He'll probably be wanting to see less of the family altogether.

"My husband, John, will be five years on into his career. That will probably bring good news – he's very successful. He will

almost certainly have been promoted. Unfortunately, that will mean that he will probably be working even longer hours. I'll see less of him, if anything. We will probably still go on holidays together. In fact, that may be the best time that I get with them. We will do our usual walking holidays – hills and pub meals are what we enjoy. I do love my food, and we all do as a family. If I got diabetes, that would seriously cramp my style! I would have to be loads more careful about what I ate, and I wouldn't enjoy having to do that under threat of bad health. I'm a nurse, and I've seen lots of diabetes up close. The walking is one area in which my weight bothers me. I'm going to have to be a lot fitter and lighter on my feet than I am now if I'm going to keep up with John and a 15-year-old boy. I refuse to be left behind by them.

"My plan has always been to get back into nursing as Craig gets older. I was heading for a pretty senior post when I left. It will take me a while to get back to this. I would feel better as a nurse if I was carrying less weight. I probably won't have to do too much physical stuff any more, but I would feel better about leading a team of nurses if I were fitter and lighter. It's just the way I feel about my role.

"So, I will sum up like this. I am going to have more time to develop myself in the next five years. I can make a decision about which way my weight goes. My love of food actually makes me want to lose weight – I couldn't bear to find out I was diabetic. I'd hate to watch what I eat because of that. I would also like to be fitter as I refuse to be left behind physically by the boys! Finally, I'd feel happier as a senior nurse if I was carrying less weight. So losing weight is important in a lot of ways – for family life, self-development, career and holidays. I don't think that knowing this will make it easy, but at least my priorities are clear."

Jackie found lots of important reasons for losing weight, but other people come up with very different answers:

"My weight doesn't stop me from doing my evening courses or going to my book group. On the other hand, I would be annoyed if I hadn't got control of my weight in the next five years. As far *as I'm concerned I am a determined and organized person, and I should be able to make things like that happen."*

"I'm not sure that my weight makes any difference to the things I really want. It doesn't stop me from travelling – and most of the places I go, people are a lot more relaxed about weight than here! And I'm pretty active, and not too overweight, so my health isn't really a problem."

"I'm a bit stuck – I can't work out what weight has to do with the important things in my life."

Don't worry if it doesn't all seem to be going to plan. People often get stuck at this point or find that they have some of the following problems:

- "I'm in two minds about this – either having lots of good reasons but still not wanting to lose weight, or not having any good reasons but still wanting to lose weight."
- "Some of the things that matter to me would make me *less likely* to lose weight!"
- "I just can't see any personally important reasons to lose weight."

We will think through all of these problems in the following sections.

What to Do with Things that Reduce Your Motivation

Being in two minds – or even having good reasons not to lose weight

It's very common for people to have some good personal reasons to lose weight and some good personal reasons not to. For example, a person might have these two reasons:

- to stay healthy so that they can enjoy life and time with their family
- to live for the moment and not worry about tomorrow

This person might be faced with a bit of a contradiction. "Staying healthy" would involve managing their eating and exercise, and "living for the moment" would suggest the opposite!

Here is another example. A person might have these two reasons:

- to be a dedicated and supportive friend
- to judge people by the person they are and not by things like their weight

It is obviously wrong to judge a person by their weight. So this person might ask, "Why am I judging *myself* by my own weight? Why do I need to lose weight at all?" They might find that the second reason gives them *less* motivation to lose weight.

These are important issues. If mixed feelings are there, it is important to be open about them. However, we can often think about mixed feelings or "demotivating" reasons in a way that sorts them out – at least a little. It is helpful to do two things: check that your reasons are "demotivating" and go against weight loss, and then decide on your "trade-offs".

Check that the reasons really do go against weight loss

Take, for example, "living for the moment", and "not judging people by their weight". It seems that both of these ideas go against weight loss. But do they really?

This is an important question, because a lot of the time these "difficult" reasons are not what they seem.

You can ask two useful questions about reasons like these:

1. Do they actually oppose weight loss when you think about it?
2. Are you sure that they really have anything to do with weight loss at all?

For example, if a person wants to "live for the moment", does that really mean that they cannot achieve weight loss? Losing weight needs a long-term commitment. It means that a person must think about what they eat and how they exercise *today* if they are going to control what they weigh *in the future*. So if a person wants to live *absolutely* for the moment, and eat what they like, and do as little activity as they feel like at the moment – then yes, this reason will not help with weight loss.

On the other hand, is a person really able to "live for the moment" if they have back pain? Is it easy to be spontaneous when you have to remember to take your medication for blood pressure or diabetes? How can you "live for the moment" if you can't really keep up with your children or friends because you are not fit enough? So, thinking it through, this reason actually can encourage weight loss.

How about "not judging people by their weight"? Most people would agree that a person's weight has nothing to do with whether they are kind, honest, intelligent or a valuable person. Losing weight does not necessarily make someone a nicer person and gaining it does not make them less valuable! It sounds as if "not judging" people by weight would take away any motivation to lose weight.

Of course, the answer is that "judging" people (or not) has nothing to do with weight change. The kindest, most valuable person in the world might well have a BMI of 40. Does the fact that they are a really lovely person make them at any less risk from diabetes or heart disease? Conversely, a really horrible person with a BMI of 40 might lose weight and not be any nicer. So this is an example of how a reason that seems to go against weight loss actually has nothing at all to do with weight. A person can passionately believe that overweight people are valuable, marvellous people (as we do) – but still understand very clearly the health risks of being seriously overweight.

Decide on your trade-offs, and be honest about what you will lose

Of course, even when you think things through, there may still be problems. This is not something to worry about. Everyone knows that almost every serious decision in life has both pluses and minuses. Thinking about "trade-offs" means that you can be clear about them and make an informed decision about them.

For example, the person who wants to "live for the moment" is going to have to make a choice between eating what they like when they like and doing as little exercise as they like and being healthy enough to be free and spontaneous.

Looking at trade-offs means being really clear about the costs and benefits of losing weight. There are nearly always costs. People almost always have to make changes to long-term patterns of eating. They also have to exercise, even if exercise isn't their favourite thing. Think hard now about everything that would be difficult about weight loss. Will you go through all that to get the rewards?

Please note! If the hard things seem absolutely terrible, then it is probably worth doing this exercise again after you have read the next two chapters.

This exercise may also be something that you come back to when times get tough. Don't worry if it is not all worked out right now.

There is one last thing to do with your reasons. Some reasons are guaranteed to leave you in two minds or not make you feel good. It's best to get rid of them altogether.

Throw Out the Bad Reasons and Throw Out the Guilt

What are the bad reasons? Here are a few:

"I really ought to lose some weight for myself."
"I shouldn't be so careless about my health."
"Let's face it, my wife won't leave me in peace until I lose some weight."

There's good research to show that any reasons with "should" or "ought" in them won't work in the long term. They won't work because *you* have to *want* to lose weight *for a good reason*.

Let's put it another way: guilt doesn't work! It may get a person started, but it won't keep them going in the long term. Guilt is a negative emotion – it may push a person into action, but it does not give energy or happiness. And what do we do with negative emotions? We avoid them. So if weight loss is about guilt, we will start avoiding thinking about weight loss.

Can you change your guilty reasons so that they are positive? For example, if you change "I shouldn't be so careless about my health" to "I choose to look after my health because it matters to me and my family", does it sound any more motivating?

If you can change your guilty reasons to positive ones, then this is great. If not, get rid of them altogether and focus on your positive reasons. This gives the best chance for success.

So Where Are You Now?

You have now looked at your real reasons to lose weight. Check through the following list to see if your reasons are going to stand up to the challenge of weight loss:

Reasons checklist

1. Are your reasons really personal and connected to the things that matter in your life?
2. Have you written them down?
3. Have you written them down in positive terms?
4. Do your reasons mean that weight loss is something you want to do for yourself, because it's important in your life?
5. Have you thrown out all of the "shoulds" and "oughts"?
6. Have you thrown out all of the guilt?
7. Have you been honest about the trade-offs involved?

At this point there are two possibilities – you have either found some important and convincing reasons to lose weight or you haven't. Read the section below that applies to you!

1. You have found some important personal reasons that you think will motivate you

This is very good news. If you have good reasons to lose weight then you will already realize that you are more likely to make a genuine effort and keep going when things get tricky.

There is one problem: reasons are easy to forget. And when we forget them, we tend to lose energy and determination. So it's important to write them down. Or you can paint them if you prefer, or use any other way of expressing yourself!

Then you need to put them somewhere where you can look at them regularly. If you prefer a big public statement, you could stick them on your fridge door. If your reasons are more of a private thing, you could keep them in your wallet or purse. Don't just limit yourself to one copy! Anything will do, so long as you have *your* reasons, in *your* words, in a place where you can see them regularly. These reasons will provide the emotional "fuel" for your journey.

When you are ready, you can skip to the summary at the end of this chapter on page 24.

2. You have not found enough good reasons, or your reasons don't really seem motivating

If you have not found enough good reasons to lose weight, then you may be right! Perhaps now is not the right time for you to lose weight. This is a good and valid decision, if you choose to take it. We are living in a society that often tells people that they need to lose weight when from a health point of view this isn't true. If you choose to stand up to this pressure, then be proud of yourself. Everyone knows that life is about more than food and weight, though some popular magazines try to tell us otherwise. Good luck!

But before you take this book back to the shop, please check one thing first. Recall the body mass index (BMI) that you calculated earlier. If your BMI is greater than 30, then please don't stop reading just yet. It may be useful for you to read the next section. It's about the health risks of being overweight.

Being Overweight and your Health: A Reality Check

Health warning! Please only read this section if:

- you have a BMI of over 30
- you went through the "Reasons checklist" and weren't left with much
- you are in a fairly good mood, and
- you are really willing to think about your health in the future

If you are not in a fairly good mood or are not sincerely interested in thinking about your health, then please leave this section and come back to it when the time is right.

If someone is overweight and they have been anywhere near a health professional, they have probably been told to lose weight for their health. They may have been threatened with diabetes and high blood pressure. But being told that you might get sick is not always helpful or motivating. It's hard for to think seriously about a vague risk some time in the future. It doesn't seem very real, or quite as important as the other things that are happening right now.

Here you can do your own very personal "reality check". You can find out for yourself whether you are ignoring some nasty surprises that might be coming up. Please remember, this is a personal thing, so only do it if you really want to check this out. If you are just trying to scare yourself into losing weight, then please go back and re-read this chapter from the beginning!

How do people deal with health risks?

Often people are surprised when they get ill, even when they haven't taken care of their health. Do you know anyone who is like this? It may be someone who is annoyed by dentist's bills even when they obviously don't take care of their teeth or someone who complains that their medication doesn't work even though they don't take it on time. How can this happen? Why don't people do the right thing for their health?

The answer is that we all have a hard time worrying about things that haven't happened yet. We tend to think, "Nothing bad has happened yet so there's no point getting worried." However, although it may seem strange, two things can often happen at the same time – an overweight person can worry less about their health risks whilst in reality their health risks are getting worse. They go for months and years without any health problems and come to think that the health risk can't be that urgent. Of course, it can actually be getting more serious as time passes.

If you are reading this section, you have a BMI of over 30. That means you are at a much higher risk of getting ill from diabetes and heart disease. If you are ill already, it could get worse. It does *not* mean that you are a bad person, or have been lazy or ignored your health. Everybody has their own personal health risks; we just happen to be talking about this one. This is your reality check.

What would health problems mean?

The other reason that it's hard to take health risks seriously is that most of us aren't doctors or nurses. So we don't know what diabetes, hypertension or hypercholesterolaemia are, or what they mean in everyday life. (If your BMI is above 30, then you're at greater risk of all of these. If your BMI is above 40, the risk is even greater.) Ask your doctor if you have any questions. However, what you really need to know is what these conditions are like and so what it's like to be ill as a consequence of being overweight. We have cut out the jargon and put down a few of the common things that happen to people who have the illnesses that go with being overweight:

- pain in the joints
- pain in the back

- inability to walk very far or very fast
- increased sadness and misery
- swollen feet and ankles
- taking pills every morning and evening (for diabetes, blood pressure)
- getting side-effects from the pills
- feeling worse about body shape
- increased tiredness
- bad sleep
- headaches
- less ability to concentrate
- feeling frightened, worried that it's not possible to get out of this situation
- having to change diet (due to diabetes)
- having to go to the doctor a lot of the time
- increased time off work
- having to go to hospital
- having to depend on other people to do things for you

There are nastier symptoms than these, but these are common.

The final reality check

Now for your final big reality check. Go back to page 12 and do the "Five Years" exercise again. When you imagine your future, try to imagine some of the symptoms above in your life. Try to do it as realistically as possible and imagine how you would feel.

We hope that this section has helped you do your own "reality check". If it has changed the way you see things, be sure to add this to your list of reasons to lose weight.

Summary

- There is a lot of talk of "willpower" when it comes to losing weight. Most of it is unhelpful.
- However, motivation is real and important – motivation keeps people going in hard patches.

Motivation to Change

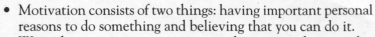

- Motivation consists of two things: having important personal reasons to do something and believing that you can do it.
- Write down your important personal reasons to lose weight.
- It is normal to be "in two minds" about weight loss. There are usually good reasons not to lose weight!
- Motivation through guilt does not work. So make your reasons positive and throw out the "shoulds".
- Check that you are very clear about the risks to your health due to being overweight. Health risks do not go away if ignored.

2

Thoughts and Beliefs

"You've got to think positively if you want to lose weight."
"Stop being so negative!"

Many people agree that the way a person thinks about weight loss will affect how successful they are. Some people seem to think that there is a "correct" attitude or that "positive thinking" is always important. We are not sure that a "perfect" attitude exists. However, we are quite convinced that some patterns of thinking are unhelpful and tend to cause people to fail.

We can all look around us and see people whose attitudes seem to make them more likely to fail. Some people never try new challenges because they are sure that they won't succeed. Others are so convinced that they are unattractive that they avoid possible romance and even push other people away when they look interested. You can probably think of many examples like this.

Patterns of thinking can often make difficult situations worse. Although it's easy to say, "Think positively," not many people can tell you exactly how to go about it. Also, you need to be sure that there is something unhelpful about your thinking in the first place. One of the great benefits of CBT is that it shows you, in practical terms, how to check if your thinking patterns are helping or hindering. It also shows you how to change your thoughts and beliefs.

However, before we start, let's be clear about which kinds of "thinking" are important for weight management. After all, the word "thinking" could be applied to doing a difficult crossword, or daydreaming in the shower, or taking a penalty kick. These are all very different mental processes!

"Automatic" Thinking Patterns

To get an idea of which types of thinking are important for weight loss, take a look at **Pete's** thinking patterns. Pete is meant to be eating healthily, but he is also very busy at work and he is due to give an important presentation later on this morning.

The alarm goes off . . .
"Oh, God, I seem to have only just gone to sleep. I haven't had enough sleep to get myself ready for this presentation. I need to get into the shower now, before I drop back off. I wish this presentation was another day. Actually, I wish that Sue could have done it, she's better at this kind of thing. I wish that I had that kind of confidence, it would make doing the presentation so much easier. I should stick to desk work and let other people do the public speaking."

Breakfast . . .
"Cereal and fruit juice. Oh, that is really depressing. On a morning like this, I could really do with a fry-up! Just when I need some energy for the day I'm only allowed to have cereal . . ."

Looking at the children's lunchboxes . . .
"That's where my problems come from. We need to have potato chips in the house for the kids and I end up eating them just because they're there. If it's in the house, I will always eat it . . ."

Dressed and ready to leave the house . . .
"Well, at least I look OK for the presentation. For a big man, at least. Look at that belly. It would all be different if I could get

27

*some exercise. I could be really fit and I'd have loads more energy.
I wish I could be fitter . . ."*

All of the time between waking up and going to work, Pete
was thinking. He was doing things the whole time and he was
having different feelings (feeling nervous and stressed, for
example), but he was constantly thinking: about the future
(mainly worrying); about himself (not being very confident
and having a big belly); and about what is fair and what is
allowed (he wasn't "allowed" a fried breakfast). There were
plans, too (to exercise), and he was trying to work out the
causes of his problems (having potato chips around the house).

Pete had not decided to sit down and think about his life that
morning. In fact he was hardly aware that he was having these
thoughts – they were just running through his mind, like having
a radio on in the background. This is the way that our minds
work much of the time. So lots of important thinking happens
automatically and we often hardly notice that we are doing it.

Unfortunately, we are usually not able to notice that our
thoughts are just thoughts – we think that they are true. This
will turn out to be a serious problem for weight loss – and for
many other parts of life. It's only when something happens to
jolt us out of our assumptions that we are able to see that it's
just our minds making judgements or having opinions.

All of our thinking could be put somewhere on the line below:

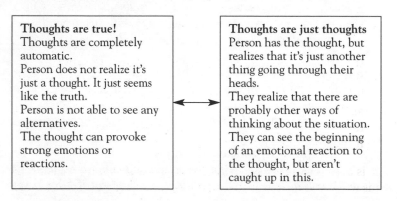

Thoughts are true!	**Thoughts are just thoughts**
Thoughts are completely automatic. Person does not realize it's just a thought. It just seems like the truth. Person is not able to see any alternatives. The thought can provoke strong emotions or reactions.	Person has the thought, but realizes that it's just another thing going through their heads. They realize that there are probably other ways of thinking about the situation. They can see the beginning of an emotional reaction to the thought, but aren't caught up in this.

Most of us spend our lives on the left-hand end of this line. This is not necessarily a problem. Lots of thinking is automatic, and that is the way that it is meant to be. It wouldn't help if we tried to analyse our thoughts every moment of the day. However, we are particularly likely to be at the left-hand end of the line if we are stressed or sad. At these times it seems that thoughts – particularly negative thoughts – are very definitely true. And this can get us into trouble.

The rest of this chapter focuses on how to move thinking to the right-hand end of the line. At the right-hand end there is more freedom, and more choices in our feelings and habits.

How automatic thinking can get us into trouble

Automatic thinking can be useful, but it can also make difficult situations worse and cause all sorts of unpleasant emotions. We can work through some of Pete's thoughts to see how they affected his mood:

- Is Pete really bad at presentations? Would he have been picked for such an important job if he was no good at it?
- Does he really need to avoid the presentation? Might it be an opportunity to practise his skills?
- Does he really need a fry-up? Or does he really need to feel less nervous?
- Is it true that he's not allowed a fry-up? Who is stopping him from having one?
- Is having potato chips in the house for the kids is part of Pete's problem? It might be. But could he do something about this problem, rather than just feeling defeated about it?
- Similarly, Pete might well be right about exercise – he could be fitter and have more energy. Could he make a plan – or at least decide to set aside some time to think about it – rather than just imagining that everything would be perfect if he could just get to the gym?

It is clear that Pete's thinking was making him nervous about his work and it was not helping him lose weight. It is important to pay attention to the fact that it was his automatic, moment-by-moment thinking that was the problem. His conscious mind was very clear – he knew that he was trying to eat healthily and he wanted to stick to it. He also knew that he had managed difficult presentations at work before. Unfortunately, when the going got tough, these were not the only thoughts going through his head. The automatic thoughts were there, too.

Strong emotions and serious difficulties change automatic thinking

Automatic thoughts are often problematic when strong emotions or "stuck" habits are present. Here are three ways in which automatic thinking goes wrong.

Thoughts are biased or untrue

Automatic thinking often puts a negative "spin" on events. A clear example is Pete's prediction that his presentation would go badly. As for weight loss, automatic thoughts will usually say that it is hopeless (how do they know?) and that a person does not have the willpower to succeed (really? They have willpower for lots of other things).

Here are some other styles that automatic thoughts can have:

1. All or nothing – for example, a person might think, "I'm doing fantastically – I've stuck to my plan," before thinking, "I've screwed it up completely. I may as well give up."
2. Catastrophic – that is when the thought says that things will always go wrong. "This new plan will be like the rest – lots of effort and deprivation and then all the weight will go back on."
3. Focused on the negatives and ignoring the positives – for example, a person will concentrate on the one "binge" that they had in the week and ignore the fact that they went to the gym just as they planned.
4. Self-blaming – for example, "I'm so stupid. I've got no willpower. Why can't I manage to lose weight?" In this style,

the person takes something that is genuinely difficult, perhaps even unavoidable, and then blames themselves and presumes that there is a problem with their own character.

All of these are classic styles of biased or untrue automatic thoughts. There are many more. You may recognize some in yourself already.

They are unhelpful

Of course, automatic thinking is not always biased. However, it can be true and still be very unhelpful. Take, for example, the thought "I've never yet managed to lose the weight and keep it off." This might be quite true. But does it really help? What would it do for someone's mood? Would it help their motivation?

They have a limited point of view

We have already noted that people tend to think that their automatic thoughts are true. Unfortunately, they also tend to think that they are the *only* truth. This may not be true!

Taking "I've never yet managed to lose the weight and keep it off" as an example once more, have a look at some other thoughts about the situation:

"I've not had much luck losing weight before, but each time I've learned a little bit more about what doesn't work."
"I've never tried to lose weight with this method before. This is a completely new thing for me."
"It doesn't necessarily matter if I lose much weight. This time I'm going to focus on my fitness, because it's so important for my health."
"I know from the NWCR study that it can take a few times before the final, successful attempt to lose weight. It took me three times to pass my driving test!"

These thoughts show that there are many different ways to view the same situation. Also, there are often many different parts of the situation to focus on.

It's not just "negative thinking" that is the problem

Many people have the view that a person should always think positively. Of course, this sounds like helpful advice, but it is not good enough for really difficult situations. First of all, it ignores that fact that positive thoughts can be really unhelpful, and second, it does not tell us *how* to change our thinking.

Take the thought: "If I just follow this fantastic new diet then I will lose all of my weight really easily and permanently!" Is this thought "negative"? No, it's a very positive thought! Is it biased or untrue? Yes, it is probably untrue. Is it helpful? No, it just leads to dreams that will probably end in failure. Is it the only way of seeing the "magical new diet" at hand? Probably not! This thought is very positive, but it as also biased, unhelpful and limited. This is the CBT approach to thinking.

As we go through the chapter, we will show you how to spot unhelpful thinking – and more importantly, how to see it for what it is and change it.

Becoming More Aware of Automatic Thinking

Our automatic thoughts can help to keep us stuck in old habits and emotions. These are often not the best habits and emotions for us. However, if we become more aware of the impact of automatic thinking on our lives, we will have more options and change will be easier.

The skills presented in the following sections of the book will allow you to be more aware of your mental habits. You will start to realize what is bothering you and holding you back. To get started, it is useful to have a look at some common negative thoughts about weight. Then we can learn how to spot them.

What automatic thoughts look like

Teaching a person to see their own thinking is a bit like teaching a young gardener how to identify a rare type of plant. The gardener needs lots of examples of what the plant looks like and they also need to know where it usually lives. This is the approach we will follow here.

Have a look at the following table. These are common thoughts in people who are trying to lose weight. Some of them may be familiar to you, some not. You will certainly have many more examples. It is important to note that these automatic thoughts are usually some kind of *statement about how things are or how they should be.*

Some Examples of Automatic Thoughts about Weight Loss

Remember, these are not necessarily untrue, but they are often biased, unhelpful, or only take a limited view of the situation.

Thoughts about what caused the weight problem

"I don't understand why I am overweight. I don't stuff myself all day."

"I don't understand why I am overweight. I don't eat any more than my friend, and she's slim."

"I may have a problem with my metabolism/my glands/the way my body stores fat."

Thoughts about what to do about the problem and what this "solution" will be like

"Losing weight will be awful – I'll be hungry/miserable/deprived all of the time."

"My life is busy and difficult enough already. I can't cope with losing weight at the same time."

"Losing weight will be awful. I'll have to go running and do aerobics and go to the gym the whole time."

"I don't want to spend my life counting calories or being some gym-mad exercise nut."

"I won't be able to go out and eat with my friends."

"I'm so overweight, I've got such a long way to go. It's too much. I just can't face it. I can't imagine getting there."

"I'm so overweight, I've got such a long way to go. I need to go on a seriously strict diet this time."

"I'm so overweight that even if I lose loads of weight I will still be fat."

Thoughts about what you "can" and "can't do"

"I can't bear feeling hungry."

"I can't bear exercise."

"I can't do this. I've tried every diet in the book and they've all failed."

"I can't do this. I'll never stick to any new regime. I'm just fundamentally weak-willed."

"I can't do this. I have a problem with my relationship to food. Something is seriously wrong and it needs fixing."

"I can't exercise until I feel better about my body."

"I can't change until my self-esteem improves/I feel less depressed/I stop bingeing."

Thoughts about what you should and shouldn't do, and what is fair and what isn't

"I shouldn't have to do this – it's not fair."

"I shouldn't have to do this – other people can eat what they like and stay slim."

"I shouldn't have to do this – it's not fair that just eating what I like makes me overweight."

"I shouldn't have to change – other people should accept overweight people more."

Thoughts that happen "on the spot" whilst trying to lose weight

"I've just broken my diet. I've blown it. I may as well give up now."

"I hate this. I want to eat right now and I'm not allowed to."

"I hate this. I don't want to spend my whole life restraining myself."

"If I eat just a little of what I want, I will lose control and ruin everything."

"I've just done a load of work, I deserve this treat."

"I've just had a miserable time, I need something to pick myself up."

"I've just done really well! That was fantastic! I deserve this."

"I'll worry about weight loss later. I'm not going to think about it now."

"I'm not going to let a stupid diet tell me what to do, I'm going to eat this."

"I don't care. I'm going to eat this."

"Food is one of the great joys in life. Why would I want to turn into a diet nut?"

Thoughts about yourself

"I'm pathetic. I can't believe I let it get this bad. I deserve to be overweight."

"My body is disgusting. I'm repulsive."

"I have stuck to my programme so I am a good person."

"I have not stuck to my programme so I am a bad person."

"I'm weak-willed/lazy/stupid."

Now you have a flavour of some of the biased, limited and unhelpful thoughts that get in the way of weight loss, we will get on to spotting some of your own thinking.

Where automatic thoughts tend to live

Being able to spot or "catch" an automatic thought is a hugely useful skill. However, it is not easy or straightforward. Like the gardener trying to spot the rare plant, it takes practice – and a little bit of good advice. We have already shown you what some automatic thoughts look like and now we will show you where they live!

Fundamentals

Unhelpful automatic thoughts live in all sorts of places, but are nearly always found:

- near strong feelings like sadness, fear, shame and anger
- near strong physical sensations like hunger, feeling full, feeling tired or feeling deprived
- near changes in feeling – for example, going from feeling calm to being a little tense or from happy to a little bit sad
- near issues and habits that are "stuck" and difficult to change

Follow your feelings

The rule here is *follow your feelings*. When you feel strong emotions or strong physical feelings, that is where you will find the most important automatic thoughts. Here are some example situations:

Deciding that you should probably start a weight-loss programme
Deciding that you look fat or unfit
Looking at "weight" material – diet books, magazines, etc
Seeing pictures of slim people or people who seem to be able to eat lots and maintain their weight
Being tempted to eat something that does not fit your weight-loss plan
Just after overeating
Starting a weight-loss programme
Trying to exercise and finding it difficult
Looking at a meal that seems to be a "small" amount of "healthy" food
Thinking about past attempts to lose weight

Think about the past 24 hours. You have probably had some kind of feelings about your weight in this time – if you're really stuck, think how some of the material in this book has made you feel! You can go back beyond the last 24 hours if you like, but try to think of a recent situation. When you have got a situation, we will move on to working out what the most important thought is and how to deal with it.

Pinpointing the most important automatic thoughts

Hopefully you have managed to find a recent upsetting situation. Now you need to put your finger on the most upsetting part of the situation and put it into words. Use your notebook here – you will need to write this all down, as it won't all fit in your head!

To get to the main automatic thoughts, you can ask these questions about your upsetting situation:

What was going through my mind just before I started to feel this way?
What does this say about me? What does it say I can/can't do?
What does this mean about me? My life? My future?
What am I afraid might happen? What is the worst thing that could happen if this is true?
What does this mean about what other people might think/feel about me?
What does this mean I should/shouldn't do?
What images or memories do I have in this situation?

Write down some answers to these questions. You may find that there is just one main answer or that there are a lot. There can be dozens of confusing thoughts in any situation. We need to be able to cut through all of the confusion and focus on the most important issue. There are two steps to "pinpointing" the thought:

1. Explain what the worse part of the problem, situation or emotion is.
2. Summarize it briefly.

This process will allow you get straight to the heart of the matter.

Step 1: Explaining the thought

Remember the rule: "Follow the feeling". It is most useful to focus on the thought that has the most emotion attached to it or the one that seems most personally important and meaningful. However, it can be hard to write this down in a way that helps. Some of the time we can look at a situation and realize that our thoughts were things like:

"Oh no!"
"Not again!"
"I can't bear this!"
"That idiot!"

Catching these thoughts is great, but we need to go a step deeper than this and work out exactly what the problem is. For example, if the thought is "Oh no!", then what exactly is wrong? If the thought is "I can't bear it!", then what exactly is it that the person can't bear? If it's "That idiot!", then what exactly did the idiot do and why does it matter? It's important to explain the issues.

For example, when the unclear thought "I can't bear it!" was pinpointed, the thought was actually: "I can't bear the thought of struggling with another diet and failing again!"

This was an example of a thought that was really too short or unclear. Of course, the problem can also run in the opposite direction. A person can try to write down a thought and end up writing pages and pages, so . . .

Step 2: Summarize the main issue

Remember, the point of this exercise is to explain and summarize the most important or upsetting aspect of a situation or feeling. If you try to write down your thought but you find that you are writing a lot, then you can probably pinpoint even further. For example:

> *"It's really a problem. Nothing has ever helped me lose weight. I have tried everything over a period of years and I'm completely*

stuck. None of the diets seem to work. I've no idea if I am ever going to shift this problem."

This can probably briefly be summarized as:

"Nothing has ever worked before and nothing ever will work."

Here is another example:

"Diets just don't suit me. Or I'm not suited to diets. Each time I've tried it has simply been torment. I've ended up thinking about food every second of the day. I just don't know how I'm going to get around this. I don't want my entire life to be wrapped up in food and calories."

This can be summarized as:

"Weight loss will be unpleasant and spoil my everyday life."

Remember, the skill here is to quickly and effectively pinpoint the heart of the problem – or what you think is the heart of the problem. This will be your main automatic thought.

How did it feel?

If you are still having difficulties working out the automatic thoughts in your upsetting situation, try holding the situation in mind and remembering exactly what it felt like. Then ask yourself how would you have completed these sentences at that time:

I am . . .
I am not . . .
I can . . .
I can't . . .
The future is . . .
I should . . .

I should not . . .
Other people are . . .
My problems with weight are caused by . . .
What I need to do is . . .
If I try to lose weight, the process will be . . .

Remember, as you complete these statements, that we are not looking for your "sensible", clever answers. The most important thing is to recognize how your mind works automatically in difficult and "stuck" situations. We need to work with your automatic mind, not your sensible mind, if change is going to happen. *Important*

What You Can Do about Unhelpful Thinking Patterns

Now that you have found one or more important automatic thoughts, you need to deal with them. There are two steps:

1. Question the thought.
2. Expand your thinking.

It is not always true that a thought – even a negative one attached to a strong emotion – is biased or untrue. The way to find out whether a thought is true is to question it.

The second step is to expand your thinking. As we noted earlier, even if thoughts are true, they usually only put across one view of a situation. Expanding your thinking is about getting more views and therefore more options for change.

Step 1: *How to question the thought*

If you have found a thought that is attached to a strong negative emotion or a "stuck" habit, then this thought needs to explain itself! It needs to be able to convince you that it is being truthful and helpful.

You can imagine that you are a lawyer in a courtroom. The thought is like someone that you are cross-examining – someone you are fairly suspicious of. Basically, you want to know 1) if the thought is biased or untrue and 2) if it is helpful or unhelpful.

When you are more practised at this, you will be able to do it quite quickly. To begin with, you will benefit from using a list of questions (below and in Appendix I) that are guaranteed to test any thought in existence.

Top 10 questions for thoughts

Important

1. What is the evidence for this thought? What is the evidence against it?
2. What are some other ways of thinking about this situation?
3. How would another person see this situation? What would I say to my best friend or someone I loved if they were in the same situation?
4. What are the advantages and disadvantages of thinking this way?
5. When I am not feeling this way, do I think about this type of situation differently? How?
6. Am I asking questions that have no answers?
7. Five years from now, if I look back at this situation, will I look at it any differently? Will I pay attention to other parts of the situation that I'm ignoring now?
8. Are there any small things that show my thoughts aren't true? Am I ignoring them or not taking them seriously?
9. Am I blaming myself for something over which I do not have complete control? Am I forgetting that other people are responsible for their own behaviour (and I'm not responsible for what they do)?
10. Am I always thinking that things will go badly? Am I exaggerating how bad things would be if they did go wrong?

These questions may not mean much without an example, so here is one from someone you have already met – **Pete.**

Later in the day Pete did his presentation. It went quite well, although he was terribly nervous. He bought himself a dough-nut and a packet of potato chips to celebrate. He enjoyed these, but afterwards became depressed about his weight. He spent some time trying to pinpoint what had made his mood drop after eating the doughnut. He decided that the thought was: "I will never manage to stick to any weight-loss plan." Pete was pretty sure that this was true. However, he decided to follow the excellent advice in this book(!) and question the thought anyway. Here are the results of his efforts:

What is the evidence for this thought? What is the evidence against it?
"Well, I suppose the evidence for this thought is that I have never managed it before. On the other hand, there have been plenty of things in my life that have been difficult that I have finally managed to do. Most people try to stop smoking a few times before they finally manage it. The evidence against it is that I have surprised myself before – done more than I thought I could."

What are some other ways of thinking about this situation?
"First, eating a doughnut and a packet of potato chips does not mean that I am doomed never to lose weight. Second, I could see things as opportunities to learn, rather than just think that I will fail – each time I try to lose weight I learn a little bit more. Third, this way of thinking really gets me down. I am fed up with all of this doom and gloom about weight. I'd like to try thinking some-thing else. Fourth, I'm still in good health. I'm a young man – there is plenty of time to keep trying."

How would another person see this situation? What would I say to my best friend or someone I loved if they were in the same situation?
"I would encourage a good friend not to give up. I would tell them that losing weight is difficult but that they had done lots of other difficult things in their lives."

What are the advantages and disadvantages of thinking this way?
"Advantages? None. Although I suppose if I expect the worst then I won't be so disappointed if it happens. The disadvantages are obvious. I call myself a failure before I have even started. It knocks down my motivation and makes me feel hopeless."

When I am not feeling this way, do I think about this type of situation differently? How?
"When I feel less miserable, then I am a bit more optimistic. I have more faith in myself and believe that losing weight is at least possible."

Am I asking questions that have no answers?
"A little. This thought can't have an answer because it is about the future. And I have no idea what might happen in the future."

Five years from now, if I look back at this situation, will I look at it any differently? Will I pay attention to other parts of the situation that I'm ignoring now?
"Well, I suppose that depends whether I have lost any weight in five years' time! Actually, maybe not. Whether I have lost weight or not, I will certainly wish I had spent less time telling myself that I was bound to fail. It's a real waste of time, whatever happens."

Are there any small things that show my thoughts aren't true? Am I ignoring them or not taking them seriously?
"Maybe. I did really mess up my eating plans for the day. But I still had a healthy breakfast as planned. And frankly, it could have been worse – it could have been a whole pizza, or burger and chips!"

Am I blaming myself for something over which I do not have complete control? Am I forgetting that other people are responsible for their own behaviour (and I'm not responsible for what they do)?
"Um, this question doesn't seem to apply to this thought."

Am I always thinking that things will go badly? Am I exaggerating how bad things would be if they did go wrong?

"Well, I'm certainly not being positive. And what if I did try another weight-loss programme and fail? Does that mean I'm doomed forever? Not really. If would be a shame, but not a catastrophe."

Pete had felt quite sure that his thought was true when he started questioning it. By the end of the process, he was much more certain that it was biased, unhelpful and rather limited.

However, the way to deal with thoughts is not just to interrogate them until they beg for mercy. The point of the exercise is to give you more freedom, more options and more ways of seeing things. The "questioning" stage is just one step on the road to expanding your thinking.

Step 2: Expanding your thinking

In this stage, the aim is to find *three alternative thoughts* about the situation. The main point is that they are different from the thought that you were having before, that's all. However, if you have just gone through the questioning stage, you will probably already have some thoughts that are more interesting and will give you more choices than your initial thought.

Let's follow Pete through this phase:

"I need to get three alternatives. What are my top three things to remember from questioning? I think they are:

1. I don't know what will happen in the future – I may surprise myself.
2. Thinking about failure all the time is depressing and gets me nowhere.
3. It could be a lot worse. I didn't binge. There is plenty of time to keep trying.

I don't think that having these thoughts will magically make me lose weight, but it's a lot better than sitting around moping about being a failure. I know that I have got options and I'm not going to limit myself by presuming that I will always fail."

Developing your Skills in Dealing with Automatic Thoughts

There is one main thing that you need to do now to move forward – and that is to practice. Like any skill that is worth having, changing your thinking will take a bit of time and effort. However, it is a skill that you will be able to use for the rest of your life. After a while, it will become easy and automatic. It applies in all sorts of situations, not just weight loss. Any time you spend developing this skill will be time well spent.

The basic steps of changing your thinking will be familiar to you now. They are:

1. *Spot* a difficult situation, *follow the feeling* and then *pinpoint* the thought, *explain* and *summarize* exactly what the issue is.
2. *Question* the thought, *expand* your thinking and keep going until you have three alternative views.

You need to start doing this regularly, day by day, and writing things down in your notebook. It is absolutely necessary to write everything down at this stage. It is quite impossible for anyone to hold a thought, 10 questions, all of the answers to those questions and three alternative thoughts in their head at once!

However, this does not mean that you will be making notes for the rest of your life. After a while this will become a new mental "habit" and you will easily be able to spot thoughts and see interesting new perspectives. However, everyone has to start slowly and carefully, doing the exercises "by the book", before real skill can emerge.

It can actually be very useful to notice your thoughts about the process of changing thoughts! Look at your thinking right now. Are you being optimistic or are you thinking, "I'll never get the hang of this"? Are you having thoughts about yourself – perhaps "I'm rubbish at this kind of thing" or "I'm really smart! I'm sure I don't need to practise." All of these are useful thoughts to spot, question and expand. You don't have to use thoughts about weight – any thought will help you develop your skills.

Some examples

Here are a couple of examples that might help you. To save space, we have just organized the "questioning and expanding" around three questions:

1. How true is this thought? Is it biased?
2. How helpful is this thought?
3. What are other ways of thinking about the situation?

Look hard at how the thought is dealt with each time. This will give you ideas for your own practice.

"I don't want to spend my life counting calories or being some gym-mad exercise nut"
How true is this thought? Is it biased?

"There are certainly calorie-counters and exercise nuts out there. And in my opinion, they don't look very happy. Fair enough – I don't want to be like that. Do I really have to be like that to lose weight? Most of those people are fairly thin and trying to get thinner – not my problem. I need to choose a food and exercise programme that I can stick to, and in my case it will have to be flexible and moderate. This means I won't lose loads of weight really fast, but it means that I can still have a life."

How helpful is this thought?

"Well, it is not a very hopeful thought – so it's not very helpful. And I'm not sure how useful it is to think that all people who lose weight are 'exercise nuts' or 'calorie counters'. First, it's not a very nice way to judge people. Second, it presumes that all methods of losing weight are extreme and intense. This is not a helpful way to think."

What are other ways of thinking about the situation?

> *"First, it is not true that all weight-loss methods are extreme. Second, it is clear that I will choose a moderate and flexible programme for myself, because I want to be able to stick to it. So, there's no real problem. Finally, I wonder if thinking that you have to be a 'nut' to lose weight helps me – or just puts more blocks in my way."*

"Losing weight will be awful – I'll be hungry/ miserable/deprived all of the time"
How true is this thought? Is it biased?

> *"Well, it's certainly true that most of the diets that I have been on have made me feel deprived and hungry. However, it may be possible to lose weight without starving myself. If I lose weight gradually and concentrate on being more active, things will be easier. Also, the plan in this book includes never 'banning' any foods. This will help. Anyway, who says that every method of weight loss is going to make me feel awful! It's not as though I've tried every method in existence."*

How helpful is this thought?

> *"Maybe this thought is trying to make sure I don't put make myself miserable again on another strict diet. In a way, it's trying to protect me. But there are definite disadvantages to thinking like this. I scare myself and make myself less likely to do something new. In fact, thinking like this is so depressing that it makes me prefer not to think about weight loss at all. And one thing is for certain: I won't fix my weight problem if I don't think about it."*

What are other ways of thinking about the situation?

> *"First, that this way of losing weight may be different – this time no foods will be 'banned' and I will be concentrating on being*

more active as well as eating differently. Second, thinking that it will be awful just makes me not want to think about it – and that will get me nowhere. Finally, maybe it's just time to try something out – just give it a go and see what happens – rather than trying to predict the future and scaring myself."

Now that you understand the basics of dealing with automatic thoughts, here are a couple of tips that can help.

Advanced Tip Number 1: Sometimes question thoughts that are obviously true

This may seem like odd advice. Clearly, there are some thoughts that are not worth challenging – like the fact that Paris is the capital of France. (This seems to be true and unbiased, fairly helpful if you are a tourist, and alternative views of the situation are not likely to get us far!) However, it is important to remember that thoughts can do a very good job of convincing us that they are true. Take, for example, this person who is in the process of pinpointing a thought:

"Well, I think that the main thought is that I can't bear to stick to a diet. I just hate feeling deprived of food, it just gives me cravings the whole time. Of course, it would help if my husband were a little more helpful about the whole process. But I think that the main thought is: 'I will hate any weight-loss regime because I will feel deprived.'"

This is a good piece of pinpointing – the person here has really worked out what she is afraid of when she thinks about a new attempt to lose weight. However, she may have also missed a thought. She seemed to think that it was "obvious" that things would be easier if her husband helped more. But perhaps this is just another thought and not true at all.

When a person realizes that thoughts like these are just thoughts, not necessarily the truth, questioning them can be very valuable. This can really help us to see things that we are missing or that we would usually need another person to point out to us.

Advanced Tip Number 2: If you are getting stuck, make sure that you are questioning a thought and not a feeling

Questioning and expanding a thought can sometimes be difficult if the thought is something like "I'm sad" or "I'm so anxious". In this case, what you have found is actually a *feeling*.

The basic difference is this:

- A feeling is an emotion or sensation that can usually be put in one word.
- A thought is an statement about how things are, or how they should be, a prediction, a view of the world, an idea about a person, the world, the future, what should or should not happen . . . There are an infinite number of thoughts, but they can very seldom be expressed in a single word once they have been pinpointed.

If you have found a feeling, that is fine, and you obviously have good emotional awareness, but you need to work out the thought associated with it. For example, what are you sad about? What has gone wrong? What do you fear is happening? Perhaps what you find is: "I'm so sad, I really can't cope with this situation." In this case, "sad" is the feeling and "I can't cope" is the thought.

Keep Practising . . .

Becoming a "thoughts expert" only comes down to a few steps: spot upsetting situations and issues, pinpoint the thoughts and question and expand your thinking. Appendix I has the whole process for quick reference. As we go through the book we will occasionally suggest that you do a "thoughts check" when you look at certain issues.

As you go through your daily life, keep looking for automatic thoughts about weight. They can be found anywhere! If you look at a shop selling your favourite food or catch a glance of your body in a changing-room mirror, you will find them there. You will be able to see them when you are sticking to a weight-loss regime and when you are slipping off a weight-loss regime. If you see a picture of yourself when you were younger and slimmer, or if you are looking in a diet book, you can spot your thinking. All the time you will become more aware of how your mind works, and this will give you more freedom to change. Self-awareness always brings more freedom. This is the topic of the next chapter.

Summary

- We are thinking all of the time – about ourselves, other people, the future, what should and should not happen . . .
- We tend to think that our thoughts are true. However, a lot of the time they are untrue or unhelpful.
- Unhelpful thoughts often come up near strong emotions or stuck habits. It is useful to learn to spot these thoughts.
- Once a thought has been found, questioning it and expanding on it can give a person more options about how they feel and what they do.

3

Self-Awareness

"Self-awareness is a good thing, but to be honest, I've got it already. I know very well that there is very little relationship between what I eat and what I weigh."

"I really don't see where self-awareness is going to get me. Surely it would be better if I could just be getting on with a diet and exercise plan?"

The last two chapters have been about thoughts and motiv-ation. By now you may well be thinking, "When are we going to actually start losing some weight?"

When a person seriously wants to lose weight, it is natural to want to "get on with it". "Diet" books often offer a "plan" that you can start straight away. However, as we have seen before, this approach will often not work for the long term. This book offers an alternative – the skills that you need to manage your own weight for the long term. It shows the way to change habits, and to make those changes stick.

This approach is to change "from the inside out". This means that a person starts off by having a clear understanding of their own eating and activity habits. Then they begin to change these habits gradually, one by one. Most other methods of weight loss try to change "from the outside in" – that is, they take a plan (diet, gym) and try to "drop" it full-scale into a person's life. However, as we all know, these new regimes often do not last for very long.

There will be more about how to change from the inside out in Chapter 6. This chapter is about understanding the basic habits that you have when you are not focusing on weight loss. When these habits change, you can begin to lose weight and keep it off.

How to Understand your Day-to-Day Habits

Of course, eating and physical exercise are not the only habits that we have. Spending money is another example of a day-to-day habit. Thinking about this can help us think about weight. Imagine that you are keen to save money. You have something exciting that you want to do – go on a particular holiday, for example. However, this is going to cost money. You look at your income and it seems that there should be money to spare at the end of each month. However, this never seems to happen – there is no spare cash for your project. It looks as though your plans for saving – and your holiday – are never going to get off the ground. How would you fix this problem? How would you find out where the money was going?

If you were going to fix your saving problem, you would need to know exactly how much money was going in and out of your bank account. You could then work out how much you were spending and what you were spending it on. You might find that your loan repayments or house bills are more expensive than you thought. Or perhaps you are spending more than you thought on clothes, music or going out with friends. Of course, knowing this might not fix the problem straight away. However, you would still be able to decide how you could make changes.

In order to lose weight, it is essential to have the equivalent of a bank statement. You need to know, in detail, how much activity you are doing each week and how much food you are eating. Then, just as a person might need to "balance" their income and their spending, you need to "balance" your eating and activity if you are going to lose weight.

Some people might think this level of detail is too much. After all, most people have some idea of how much they eat.

Surely "bank statements" are not really necessary. However, when the issue is looked at closely, we really do need more information than our memories alone can give us.

Try to answer some of these questions:

1. What did you have for breakfast four days ago? And lunch? And dinner? What snacks did you have between meals?
2. And on that day, how many minutes did you spend walking?

Most people, if they are being honest, would find it very hard to answer these questions with any accuracy.

Also, many overweight people are baffled by the fact that they do not stuff themselves the way they imagine an over-weight person would. However, it is clear that a person does not need to stuff themselves to put on weight. Small increases in quantity, or in how often a food is eaten, will result in long-term weight gain. Equally, decreases in activity will do the same. A person who shifts from walking to the bus stop to taking the car may not think much about the change. However, over a year, this would make a real difference to the amount of energy they burn.

Getting an Accurate Record of Activity and Eating

One of the biggest challenges of weight loss is that we do not have an accurate record of eating and activity to help us to analyse the situation. However, we can make one. The information can be written down, dictated onto tape or recorded in some other way. The method does not matter. The important thing is that this is a living, fascinating record that includes feelings, thoughts, urges and all of the situations and habits that go with them.

Recording eating and activity is an active process. Whilst you are recording your habits, you will also be developing self-awareness. This will begin to change your behaviour. Imagine that you were spending too much money every month. You then decided that you were going to write down every penny that you spent. If you did this honestly, you would immediately begin to spend less because you would become more aware of each time that you were overspending. This effect has been shown in many scientific studies – as soon as we become more aware of our behaviour, it tends to change. So recording habits is a good way to gather information, but it is also the beginning of change.

Situations, Moods and Behaviour – How to Record Habits

What kind of recording will help a person understand their habits better? What kind of things would they have to record and how would they do it?

To answer these questions, it is a good idea to look at the kind of results that we want to get. What would it be like to understand our habits?

Kirsty has been recording her habits for about three weeks and is getting some very useful information.

"There were some surprises when I started recording my eating. I knew a couple of things already – first that my meals seemed pretty healthy (to me, at least), and second that I did tend to eat a bit more when I was feeling low. I hadn't expected to find that I ate more when I was in a good mood, though. When I was out with friends, I tended to enjoy myself and eat whatever I wanted. That tended to be quite a lot, and tended to be quite fatty foods like pizza and garlic bread.

"I was mainly right about my meals. They are quite healthy. However, I do eat quite a lot. My first plate is always a sensible size, but I didn't realize that I almost always go for seconds. That adds a lot when you do it most days. I was also right about feeling low and eating more. At least, I was almost right – I actually eat more when I am feeling stressed. I seem to use it as a kind of reward for surviving busy times.

"Snacks are a bit more of an issue than I had thought. I have a very clear plan for biscuits at work. These are a problem,

because there are always loads lying around. My plan is never to have more than two at a time with any cup of tea or coffee. I thought that this would mean I would end up only eating a handful a week. It turned out to be a little more than that. If I have three cups of coffee a day, five days a week, that's 30 biscuits a week, or over 100 biscuits per month. This isn't what I had planned – I may need to review my biscuits rule!

"I also had clear plans for exercise. (I had so many clear plans, I was really getting baffled why the weight wasn't going.) My plan was to go to a fitness class twice per week. In reality, this happened about once per week. There seemed plenty of reasons not to go. There wasn't one mood or situation that stopped me going – instead almost anything could be a reason not to go. When I was in a good mood, I would tend to think, 'Life is too short for the gym,' and see some friends instead. When I was in a bad mood, I just couldn't face it, particularly seeing my body in the mirrors in the gym.

"The rest of my activity levels are pretty typical for someone who works at a computer terminal in an office. (That is, they are pretty low.) I drive to work. I spend most of my time at work sitting. I take the lift to and from my floor. I eat lunch at my desk or take the lift to the canteen. When I come home in the evening, I mainly sit (TV and listening to music). Plus I have the occasional glass of wine – more calories, and it tends to make me feel tired and less like being active the next day. So, I probably spend a total of about two hours per day actually on my feet. That's two hours out of 24 – only two hours actually holding my body upright against gravity.

"Recording habits has not always been a pleasant experience. It has told the truth – there is more food than I thought and less physical activity. I suppose I could get upset and feel guilty about this, but I can't be bothered. It's a first step. I don't know what I'm going to do about it yet, but at least I have a place to start from."

Most people would agree that Kirsty is in a much better position now she knows these things – she is much more likely to make changes that will be effective. She got these results by recording just three things for both activity and eating:

Situations – where she was, what she was doing, whom she was with
Moods and physical feelings – what was going on in her emotions and in her body
Behaviour – what she actually did, in detail

These three things are the backbone of all of the recording that you need for weight loss.

A typical eating record

It is easiest to understand how to record eating and activity habits by seeing a good example of a record. This is a small section of an eating record written by Kirsty on a slightly boring Saturday when she was cleaning up and expecting visitors.

Situation and time	Mood or sensation	Eating
12.05. Between bits of housework and paying bills. On my own.	Bored	One tin of baked beans on two slices of brown toast. Low-fat spread.
1.40. As above. Had just watched some TV for a break (bad TV).	Bored Irritated by TV	Three crackers, with – best guess – three tablespoons of houmous on them.
2.40. Finished cleaning. House now officially ready for guests!	Pleased Relieved	Four chunks of chocolate (the usual stuff) with my cup of coffee, and two biscuits.

Although this is only a small piece of a record, it is already useful. For example, it is clear that Kirsty does have quite healthy meals. However, she also snacks quite often (on this boring Saturday, at least). There are two snacks within three hours of eating. Further records would show whether this has to do with her being bored or it being a Saturday (when she is not at work), or the cleaning up and doing housework. When Kirsty understands this, she will be able to think about how to change it.

Later on in this chapter there are some specific ideas about how to record activity and eating. They need slightly different approaches. However, there are some general ideas about how to record the behaviour that are useful in all situations.

General Principles for Good Recording

Recording situations

As you can see from Kirsty's record, it is not necessary to write down absolutely everything about a situation. Only a summary is needed. However, there are some things that are generally interesting and worth recording.

It is often important which other people are around – and it is certainly important if there are *no* other people around. Being busy is also very different from having nothing to do, so it is sensible to record this. Also, it clearly matters where you are – if you are at home, or at a restaurant or late-night store. The time of day can be very important, particularly for people who tend to snack at night. Alcohol is another really important issue – most of us are likely to eat more when we have been drinking. Of course, if there are other situations that seem to be important in your habits, then it would be a good idea to record these as needed.

Recording moods and sensations

Record all moods. It is clearly important to know how emotions affect habits (they almost always do). Sad, happy, stressed, angry and disgusted are all moods.

Also include physical sensations in this column. It is very important to record sensations like food cravings, feeling hungry, feeling full, feeling tired or feeling bloated. These are not really emotions, but may have important effects on habits.

57

Recording behaviour

The main tips here are to leave nothing out and to be as precise as possible. It is really important to describe any behaviour clearly, so that another person who did not know the situation would have a chance of understanding it properly. For example, different people mean different things by "going for a swim". Some just mean being in a pool and splashing about a bit. Others storm up and down the pool as if they were in the Olympics. These are very different forms of behaviour and they should be recorded in a way that is clear.

Amounts Count

Another very important rule in recording behaviour is that Amounts Count. Small amounts of food, or of exercise, can make a huge difference in the long term. Earlier, we saw how a small change in the standard size of a packet of crisps could make a big difference to a person's food intake over time. So it is important to record amounts.

It is also important to record drinks. Alcoholic drinks have a lot of energy in them and soft/fizzy drinks that are not diet drinks contain huge amounts of energy. If having sugar in coffee or tea is a regular habit, it is worth recording.

This may sound daunting, but you do not need to weigh your food or to time your activity to the second. There has to be a balance between recording amounts precisely and going "over the top" with exact recording. The way to find this balance is to use the "three-quarters rule".

The three-quarters rule

The three-quarters rule is simple, but it can apply to most situations: you should record quantities precisely enough to be able to clearly see an increase or a decrease of *a quarter* in that amount. For example, if a person recorded that they had eaten "a bowl of pasta", without knowing what size of bowl it was, it would be impossible to say if the amount had gone up or down by a quarter. If this person just wrote "one of my big red bowls", then it would be much more exact and they would have an idea of what a quarter more or less would look like.

Similarly, if a person wrote that they "went for a quick walk", it would be impossible to know if this had increased or decreased by a quarter. If they recorded that they "walked for 30–35 minutes", this would be just about good enough because it obeys the three-quarters rule. More detail would probably not add much.

Recording Activity

Two recording forms – one for activity, and one for eating – are included in Appendix I, and you are welcome to photocopy more for your own use. This section will explain how to use the form for activity to get as much useful information as possible.

It is easiest to show this with an example. Below we show a form that has been filled in for an average day of work for Kirsty. Have a look at it – it will mainly explain itself, but we will go through it in more detail below.

Time	Situation	Moods or sensations	Activity
03.00		Asleep	
04.00			
05.00			
06.00			
07.00	Shower, breakfast	Tired!	Stand for 20 mins – in shower and having breakfast
08.00	Car	"	Sitting
09.00	At my desk	Busy, concentrating	"
10.00	"	"	"

Time	Situation	Moods or sensations	Activity
11.00	Tea break, chatting	More relaxed	Stand for 10 mins
12.00	At my desk	Busy	Sitting
13.00	Lunch break, gone out	Relaxed, happy	Walk for 15 mins, climb 3 flights of stairs
14.00	At my desk	Busy, stressed	Sitting
15.00	"	"	"
16.00	"	"	"
17.00	Car	Tired, headache	"
18.00	Got home! TV	Relaxed, happy	"
19.00	Making dinner	Irritated	Standing for 30 mins
20.00	TV/chatting – not going to gym	Distracted	Sitting
21.00	"	"	"
22.00	"	"	"
23.00	"	"	"
24.00		Asleep	
01.00		"	
02.00		"	

Important automatic thoughts:	I'm exhausted, I need to rest.
Pedometer reading:	

Kirsty's record is quite simple. It just records situations, moods and behaviour. However, it is useful to look at how she has recorded her activity. Most people who work in an office sit down most of the day. (Of course, Kirsty stood up and walked around a bit whilst she was working, but it did not amount to much, so she just recorded it as "sitting".) However, there is a big difference between sitting and standing. It may not seem like much of a difference, but anyone who tries standing up for a whole working day – eight hours – will certainly know the difference! The same goes for walking. Try standing for an hour and then try walking briskly for an hour – there is a huge difference. And this translates into a big difference in the amount of energy a person burns. So, when recording activity, it is useful to record at least these five levels:

1. Sitting down or lying down
2. Standing
3. Walking
4. Moderate exercise – walking rapidly or doing vigorous housework or gardening
5. More intense exercise – jogging or exercising in the gym

If you want to record more than this, you can. For example, it can be a good idea to record the number of flights of stairs you have climbed or how intense your activity was – for example, a slow walk or a quick walk.

Kirsty's recording tells her a lot. It is clear that when she is at work, she does not move much. In fact, she is not really able to because her job keeps her right in front of her computer. If she were going to increase her activity, it would have to be in her breaks, in the evening or on her way to and from work. Also, there does not seem to be much of a relationship between her mood and her activity. She was more active – that is, not sitting – when she was both relaxed (lunch) and irritated (dinner), which does not seem to form much of a pattern. She avoided going to the gym by getting distracted in front of the TV – this is something that she could work on if she had the right motivation. All of this information comes from just one day's record.

At the bottom of the form, there are two extra sections. There is a space to write any important automatic thoughts that come up during the day and a section for a pedometer reading. A pedometer is an electronic device that can tell you how many steps you have taken in a day. It is very useful for measuring activity. There will be more about pedometers in the next chapter.

It is best to record activity as you go through the day. However, you could also write the whole record in the evening. It does not take a lot of effort. It took Kirsty about five minutes to record her day's activity.

Recording Eating

Recording eating is a little different from recording activity, as it is easier to record what is eaten rather than what happens in each hour. The recording forms that we recommend for eating are a little different and again are in Appendix I. Otherwise, the recording is very similar – it just covers situations, moods and behaviour. This is a sample of Kirsty's eating record:

Situation and time	Mood or sensation	Eating
06.45 Breakfast.	Tired, not very hungry	Big bowl of cereal, skimmed milk. Big glass of fruit juice.
09.00 Making coffee at work.	Tired, reluctant	Two biscuits, coffee with milk and sugar.
10.30 Another coffee (break from computer work, quick chat with colleagues).	More awake	Two biscuits, coffee with milk and sugar.
13.00 Lunch with friends.	Relaxed, happy	Chicken baguette (about 10 inches long!) with mayo and salad. Packet of crisps. Yoghurt, small pot. Another coffee (milk and sugar) with a biscuit.

Situation and time	Mood or sensation	Eating
15.00 Mid-afternoon break. Walk to canteen.	Stressed, rushed	Medium-sized flapjack.
16.30 Final coffee of the day.	Stressed	Two biscuits.
17.45 Just got home.	Relieved	Slice of toast with peanut butter.
	Headache Hungry	Being honest – also two big teaspoons of peanut butter snacked from the jar . . .
18.30 Dinner in front of the TV alone.	Irritated	Pasta in a tomato sauce (big plate). Parmesan on top. Half a baguette of garlic bread.
20.00 Watching TV	Distracted	Glass of wine. Slice of toast with peanut butter.

Important automatic thoughts:	I'm really busy. I deserve some biscuits.

Again, looking at this record gives Kirsty useful information, even though it only covers a day. We can see that her meals are fairly healthy, although it is always useful to think about the amount that she eats. However, it is clear that she eats a lot of foods that are high in energy between meals. On this day, it adds up to six biscuits, two slices of toast and peanut butter – plus more peanut butter from the jar – and a flapjack. If this is an average day for Kirsty, this would mean that she is getting through 180 biscuits a month, 60 slices of toast, 120 big teaspoons of peanut butter and 30 flapjacks. Of course, she would not eat exactly the same every day, and it would be better to look at a couple of weeks of records to get a clear picture.

However, it is clear that if she could even just eat half of that number of biscuits and slices of toast (and stop snacking peanut butter from the jar), she would make a big change over six months.

There are not many really clear links between Kirsty's moods and her eating. However, the thought that she recorded is one clue. "I'm really stressed. I deserve a biscuit" is a classic "permission-giving" thought – combine this thinking with work stress, and Kirsty will eat a lot more . . .

How to Do It

Hopefully, it is now clear why recording is useful, and roughly how it can be done. However, it can be hard to do. Like all other changes in behaviour, doing it in the middle of a busy life presents challenges. This section contains some ideas that can make things easier.

How to do the recording

As already mentioned, we have included a number of blank record forms for you to photocopy. However, you do not have to use them. You can collect information in any way that you like. Some people prefer to use a small notebook, which has the advantage of being compact and easy to carry. Remember, this book is about self-management – you can use your own initiative to come up with an alternative. However, make sure that your alternative is not less accurate and is not a "short cut". Recording behaviour is worth doing, and it is worth doing well.

When to do it

Many people have busy days and it is not easy to see when they could fill in forms. It can be particularly hard if someone wants to fill in their form in private. However, if they use their initiative, these difficulties can all be dealt with. Recording behaviour really takes very little time. About ten minutes a day is usually all that is needed and there are few people (if they are being honest) who could not find this time.

It is best to record behaviour as you go along so that it is as accurate as possible. Alternatively, you can make a record at the end of each day. However, the recording absolutely has to be done on the same day. Leaving it to the next day will not work, as memory quickly fades.

How long to do it for

It is not necessary to record behaviour forever. The point of it is to give useful information about habits and also to build habits of self-awareness and self-observation. So recording needs to be done for a while and then it can be stopped. It is often useful to go back to it, though, if you get "stuck" with weight loss or start to regain weight and do not know why.

We recommend that people record their behaviour for *four weeks*. You can choose whether you are going to record both eating and activity at the same time, or do one at a time. It is up to you – this is a self-management approach and you can make the decision. However, it is important that you cover both eating *and* activity. If you just record one of the two, it is like looking at a bank statement and only analysing the money going in, not the money going out. This approach would be quite useless in understanding a money problem. It is the same for a weight problem.

Common Problems and Difficulties

In our clinical experience, some people do find recording difficult. They are often reluctant to do it. Here are some positive ideas to help out with the most common problems.

"I really don't have the time to do this"

This is a common concern. Many people have busy lives and do not want to add anything else to their schedules. However, it is useful to "question and expand" the thought. Is this really true that you don't have time? In fact, there is almost no one who does not have a spare ten minutes in their day. Most people, if they are really honest, and really want to, can find the time.

When a person thinks "I don't have the time", this is often not what is really going on. In fact, what they actually mean is "This is not a priority for me at the moment" or "I am not willing to give up any time to do this".

If a person seriously wants to find ten minutes in their day, they will do it. If they are not willing to, that is their choice – and it is a perfectly valid one.

If you are having difficulties seeing recording as a priority, then we suggest that you go back and look at the "reasons" you found in Chapter 1. See if looking at these makes any difference to your priorities. On the other hand, if you just don't think recording will help, keep reading – we will come to this soon.

"I can't bear it, I'm just too embarrassed"

Many people feel deeply ashamed of their eating and exercise behaviour. For a person like this, writing down what they do and then seeing it on paper in front of them can be very difficult. It can increase their sense of guilt or their belief that they are a "bad" or "weak-willed" person. They would much prefer to avoid the whole thing.

This is a difficult issue to deal with. However, it is an important one to look at. This kind of shame is the sort of thing that keeps people overweight. Quite simply, if a person cannot bear to think about their problem, they avoid thinking about it; by avoiding thinking about it, it usually gets worse; and as it gets worse, they feel worse about it and want to avoid it even more. It is very easy to see how this vicious cycle keeps people overweight.

However, the opposite cycle – a positive cycle, not a vicious one – can also happen. If a person begins to deal with their problem, they can feel more confident and it may get a little better, allowing them to feel better. As they feel better, they will be more able to think about it. This can be wonderful and release people from a lot of shame.

The first step here is to pinpoint the thoughts that were associated with the feelings of shame – and to keep finding them and pinpointing them during the recording. These thoughts are often biased, limited and unhelpful. So keep questioning and expanding this thinking until newer, more helpful alternatives can be found.

"It won't help me" or "I've done it before and it didn't work"

Again, the first step here is to see these problems as thoughts, not realities, and to use your "question and expand" skills on them. Whilst many people have kept food diaries in the past, most people have not tried recording in the way described in this chapter. And remember, this is meant to work by giving you information and improving your self-awareness – it is not meant to be a magic cure. However, here are some other ideas about this problem.

If you do not think that recording will help, or you are convinced that you know it all already, then that is fine – you may be right. But there is only one way to find out. There is an experiment that you can do to see if you are right. This experiment has just three easy steps:

1. Write down everything you ate last week and the amount of time that you were active (sitting, standing, walking, exercising). Write down quite exact quantities. Don't leave anything out.
2. Now monitor your eating and activity for this week. Use the forms and do it well.
3. Compare the two – your guesses for one week and your recordings for the next week.

If your recording is really no more accurate than your memory and really does not add any understanding at all, then there are two possibilities. First, you are a very rare person who really does know all of their own habits inside out and can remember the quantities of food they ate last week in detail. You can skip the rest of this chapter! Second, you may be on a very rigid and precise regime for food and exercise, which we would recommend that you reconsider, as most people cannot keep these up for long and don't have much fun when they do.

"I really don't want to mess about with forms and records. It's not really my kind of thing"

Writing things down on paper every day is certainly not everybody's idea of fun. Many people try to make sure that there are as few forms and records in their lives as possible. This is an important block to recording.

Imagine you are a running coach. A person comes to you saying that they plan to be a brilliant 10,000-metre runner. They want to do it well and win prizes. However, after the first couple of weeks you realize that they are doing no training. You confront them with this. They say to you, "Yeah, but I find this training thing a bit boring. You see, I'm a bit of a free spirit. I'm not the kind of person who likes rules or schedules. And to be honest, your programme is a bit hard-core. I mean, training every day! It's not really my thing."

What would you say to them? It would probably be something like, "Well, I understand that it's hard work and it may be a bit new and a bit of a shock to you. However, if you want the results, this is pretty much the only way to do it. Of course, if you've decided that you don't want to be a runner any more, that's fine. There is no point in you training – that's your choice. But if you want the prizes, this is definitely the way forward."

Think about this.

"What if someone finds the record or sees me making it?"

It is true that it could be embarrassing if someone found that you were making eating or activity records, particularly if they showed that you were eating a lot. Many people still think that it is acceptable to tease or humiliate people for being overweight – and for trying to lose weight. Most people would prefer that others did not see their records.

This is not a huge problem – it just requires a bit of initiative. Everybody owns something that they would prefer other people not to see. Most people carry things around with them in wallets or bags that are not meant to be seen or used by other people. We are all able to find a way to keep things secret.

If you are struggling with this, remember that you can change the way in which you record things. You can use sheets of paper, or a small notebook, or a tape recorder/dictaphone, or make notes on a computer. Choose the way that works best for you and that makes you feel most comfortable.

How to Make Sense of It All

If you do the recording well, you will be left with pages and pages of information. You may be able to look at these pages and easily see your habits. You may immediately begin to get ideas about things that you can change. On the other hand, it can be hard to make sense of the information that you have collected. It can just seem like a big jumble of paper. Here are some ideas that will help you make sense of what you have recorded.

Look for the Big Things

The easiest way to analyse your records is to concentrate on each part at a time – behaviour, moods and situations. You can start by focusing on the column on the right – the column in which you record eating or activity. Start by focusing on the Big Things – by this, we mainly mean times when you eat large amounts (either all at once, or over a long period) and times when you are inactive (sitting or lying down) for a long period. These are usually important for weight control, as they are the times when we take in a lot of energy and then fail to burn it off.

As well as Big Things, it can be useful to look for Broken Plans. Many of us have very good intentions when it comes to food and exercise. We plan to eat moderately and healthily and to be active regularly. However, when it comes to the actual moment, things often go wrong. These are really important moments. They will show us the situations and moods in which our plans go wrong, and therefore give us an idea about how to do something about them. It will be most interesting to see the moods and situations that go with Broken Plans.

Finally, it is important to look at Overall Amounts. If a person is overweight, then this will be mainly caused by the fact that they are taking in more energy than they are burning off. So thinking about Overall Amounts is important. Even if your eating seems to be quite moderate and healthy, if you are overweight, then you are not burning off that amount regularly enough. The overall balance will have to change if your weight is going to change.

Moods and physical sensations

Now have a look at the "Moods and sensations" column in your records. Have an overall look at these columns first. You may be surprised at your moods across the day. It is common for people to look at their records and notice that they are a lot more angry, for example, or stressed, than they tend to think. It is sometimes not clear what to do about this, but at other times it can be practical information – perhaps you need a holiday more than you thought, for example!

When looking at moods and sensations, try to see if any regularly turn up next to Big Things or Broken Plans. For example, a person might find that a day full of boredom tends to go along with continuous snacking. Feeling tired might go along with breaking plans for exercise. These are fairly obvious examples – see if you can find your own.

Finally, have a look at the thoughts that go with these moods or sensations. This will often complete a very useful picture of what is happening with Big Things or Broken Plans.

Situations – look at times and places

The same applies to situations – look for situations that go with Big Things and Broken Plans. Look hard at particular times and places – for example on your own or in company. Some people find themselves snacking or bingeing at night. Others find that they give in to cheap fast food when paying for their fuel in a service station. Look particularly at the situations in which you seem to be most vulnerable.

The timing of eating and activity can be important. If a person leaves a long time between meals or snacks, they are much more likely to overeat afterwards. Look at your records and see where the largest "gaps" between meals or snacks are, and how much you eat afterwards. Also, are you more likely to break plans for activity or exercise at particular times or in particular situations? Many people find that they can exercise in the evenings, but only if they do so just after they get in from work. If they leave it too long, they are unlikely to do it. These are all important pieces of information. Try to notice your own patterns.

Useful Information

Everything that you pick up from your records about Big Things, Broken Plans or Overall Amounts of food or activity is useful information. Write it down. It is the starting-place for changing from the inside out.

However, by making all of this effort you have done more than just collect information. You have developed the skills that you need to understand your own habits. You can use these skills and techniques at any time in the future. It is often the case that people get "stuck" with weight loss. They may do well for a while, but then find that their progress stops or that they start to go backwards. The best thing to do in this situation is to start recording again for a while. It will often give you the information you need to get restarted.

Now you have done the important basic work for weight loss – looking at motivation and thinking patterns, and developing self-awareness. Next we will look at how to make real changes.

Summary

- This book shows you how to change from the inside out – that is, how to understand your current habits and begin to change them.
- To do this, you need to understand your habits of eating and activity.
- The only way to do this well is to record them, and to include important information like situations and moods.
- Analysing your records can give you important clues about your habits and doing the recording will build good habits of self-awareness.

PART TWO

How to Do It

4

Changing Physical Activity

"To say I hated sport at school would be an understatement. The humiliation of never being picked for a team, the cruel comments from other people in my class and the horror of having to get undressed and showered with everyone else . . . Now whenever I think it would be a good idea to start going to the gym, all these memories come flooding back."

When you think of physical activity is this the sort of thing that comes to mind? Unfortunately, negative experiences of activity are rather common and not just in children or adults who struggle to control their weight but also in those who may not be particularly talented at competitive sports. Child experiences can have a lasting impact on how you feel about being more active in adulthood, although it is important to say that some overweight children and adults have positive experiences of sports and exercise and gain enjoyment from their experience. However, it can be helpful to consider what kind of experiences you have had and whether this might be stopping you from being more active today.

So what does activity mean to you? Does it mean:

- Taking up a sport
- Having to be competitive
- Being totally exhausted at the end
- Doing it but hating every minute

- Spending hours in the gym every day
- Wearing tight, uncomfortable clothing
- Feeling vulnerable
- Feeling you're just no good at sports
- Being surrounded by people who are very fit and slim and don't understand your situation

These are very common beliefs and experiences, but it doesn't need to be this way. Being more active can mean:

- Reducing time spent being inactive
- Changing the way you might get from one place to the next
- Spending 10 to 15 minutes being active a couple of times a day
- Feeling more energetic
- Feeling less stressed and anxious
- Doing something you enjoy and have developed a skill at
- Sleeping better
- Feeling more positive about yourself

There is a common belief that for activity to help with weight control it needs to be some sort of structured exercise like going swimming or jogging, attending exercise classes or working out at the gym. These options are good ones for some people; if they choose this exercise and enjoy it, it will be a positive experience. However, for others these types of activities would be a struggle.

Just trying out an activity because you've been told it's good for weight loss may not be the best idea. Let's turn to **Pete's** story again:

> "My doctor had suggested I start swimming two or three times a week as a way of improving my fitness and weight. The thought really didn't appeal, but then I was desperate to lose weight so decided to bite the bullet and give it a go. It took a few weeks to build up the courage to go to the local pool and I kept telling myself that everything was going to be OK and I was really going to enjoy

this, but deep down I think I always knew this wasn't going to be my thing. Once I was in the pool and swimming I was fine and I actually quite enjoyed the feeling of moving my body more, but the whole thing was spoilt by feeling so self-conscious. It felt as if everyone was looking at my body as I walked from the changing room to the pool and this brought back all sorts of old memories from school. The most difficult part was trying to get down the steps into the water and then back up again. I managed to persuade myself to go for about three weeks but mentally it was incredibly hard work and that self-conscious feeling got the better of me in the end. By week four I'd given up, vowing that it was pointless trying to exercise. I just couldn't do it."

Although in the long run it would be helpful for Pete to work on changing his beliefs about what others might be thinking (*see Chapter 8*), it would also be helpful to choose an activity he felt more comfortable about.

Interestingly, activities that are commonly thought of as not making much of a difference when trying to lose weight, like trying to walk more often than usual, are particularly helpful ways of increasing overall activity and are less likely to be linked with some of the negative feelings described above. So it is very important to broaden what people usually think of as "physical activity". What about walking, gardening and vigorous housework?

The key to becoming and remaining more active is to choose activities that are likely to be enjoyable rather than things that have to be done for the sake of weight loss. This chapter aims to help you in choosing the approach that is most likely to work for you over the long term.

Is Changing Physical Activity Really That Important?

Activity is just as important in maintaining health and managing weight as eating healthily. However, it is often given little attention.

Here some of the benefits of activity for the body and mind:

- an improved sense of well-being – the "feel-good" factor that many people describe after activity
- a sense of achievement
- clearer thinking and memory
- improved anxiety, stress and mood
- improved sleep quality
- improved strength, mobility and flexibility
- a reduced chance of developing chronic health problems such as heart disease, high blood pressure, high cholesterol, colon cancer, breast cancer and diabetes
- for people with existing heart disease, diabetes and high blood pressure, a potential improvement in how well the condition is controlled
- a maintenance of muscle during weight loss (so helping to keep metabolism as high as possible and burning as much energy as possible)

All of these benefits are important, although some are likely to be more relevant to you than others. It can be difficult sometimes to continue being enthusiastic about the importance of activity when the benefits (like reduced risk of heart disease) won't be experienced for another 10 to 20 years. This is why the immediate benefits – sleeping better, feeling less stressed and anxious and being positive about making a change – are so helpful in maintaining the belief that activity is worthwhile continuing.

Lisa's story shows the pleasure that taking time out and including more activity can achieve. Walking was not an activity that she had thought of as exercise or something that would make much difference to her weight, but when her doctor advised her that this could be the way forward she thought she might as well give it a go. The difficulty was finding the time to be active with a busy job and a young family. In the end she decided to walk to the local park – which was about 10 minutes from the office – during her lunch hour. On some days she'd sit

and have her sandwiches there, maybe walk round the
she felt like it and then head back to the office. She would feel
so much more refreshed when she was back at her desk and
although she'd been worried about taking this time out she felt
she worked better for having had a break.

What Lisa really began to enjoy was the time on her own,
something she never really experienced at home anymore – she
had time to think about things and clear her head. What the
walking was doing for her weight almost stopped mattering; it
just made her feel so much better.

The enjoyment that activity can bring is often forgotten,
especially if you have negative memories of exercise. However,
experimenting to see if an activity suits can be the first step to
a positive experience!

The role of activity in keeping weight off

Activity can help with weight loss, but its most important role is
in helping keep weight off once it has been lost. There is some
research that suggests regular activity can help people be more in
tune with their hunger signals. This means that they may come
to prefer healthier foods, in particular foods high in starchy
carbohydrates such as bread and cereals. So the more active
someone is, the better set up they are to make healthier food
choices and to cope with the challenges of managing weight.

In the introduction to this book, we mentioned the weight-loss
"experts" of the National Weight Control Registry (NWCR). In
order to keep weight off successfully, many of them gradually
built up their activity levels until they spent about an hour a day
being active. This amount of activity seemed to be key in helping
to keep their weight lower.

An hour of activity each day may sound daunting if you're not
doing much activity at the moment. But very few people on the
NWCR will have started out doing that much. They would
have gradually increased their level of activity over time as they
became fitter and as weight was lost.

So what is the best way to get active?

Knowing What Not to Do

Unfortunately, the bad experiences that some people have with activity and exercise often leave them with unhelpful ideas about how to go about getting active. These need to be thought about first, as they can lead to difficulties.

"Right, I'm going to become really active right now"

This is a very common approach that is often short-lived and usually results in a rapid return to old habits.

Jackie was determined to lose some weight and believed that to make a difference she needed to go running every morning for at least 30 minutes. It had been some time since she had done any running – or any activity at all – so this was going to be quite a change. On Monday morning she was up an hour earlier than usual and on the road in her jogging gear at 7 a.m. She was feeling very positive and determined. All went to plan for about the first five minutes, but as she carried on running she became more and more out of breath and her legs felt like jelly. After 10 minutes she was totally exhausted, felt sick and needed to sit down on the pavement. Although she managed to go running each morning for the rest of the week she felt she hadn't reached the target she had set herself and what she was doing really wasn't "good enough". By the second week she was really struggling, her aching limbs were making getting out of bed every morning much harder and she felt really tired all the time. By week three she'd given up the jogging as a bad idea and returned to her usual inactive lifestyle.

Being determined and enthusiastic about being more active is important. However, this can mean that you set very tough targets for yourself. Trying to do too much too soon can result in giving up completely. It's usually helpful to check that the changes you choose are realistic not just in the first few weeks when changes are high priority but also over the long term. (Check out Chapter 6 for more details of how to make *smart* changes.) Changes to activity, particularly if you have been fairly inactive for some time, must be started slowly and built up gradually. Doing too much too soon is likely to result in physical symptoms like Jackie experienced and this can be very off-putting.

"I really need to 'feel the burn' if this is going to work"

There is a common belief that for activity to be beneficial it needs to be very hard work and to hurt – no pain, no gain. This is simply not true; activity really isn't meant to hurt. Indeed, pushing too hard and "going for the burn", particularly if you're not fit at the time, can risk injuries to muscles and joints as well as put you off activity on a regular basis. A little muscle soreness the day following activity is to be expected when you first start being more active, but if you're in pain while exercising you should stop. Working at a pace that is comfortable for you will not only result in all the benefits to health, fitness and weight but will be a more enjoyable experience and therefore one you'll want to continue.

How do you know when you're working at a good pace but not overdoing it? A good rule of thumb is the "talk test". If you're breathing harder than usual but you can still manage to say a few sentences without gasping for air then you're likely to be working at a good pace.

"A couple of weeks of activity will change my body shape and size"

Expecting too much too quickly is very understandable but can lead to frustration and a feeling that being more active just isn't working. It is human nature to want visible results overnight, but it is important to try and make sure you don't have unrealistic expectations of what can be achieved.

Activity is unlikely to make a big difference to weight in the first few weeks unless large amounts of activity are being done, and for most people this is neither realistic nor wise.

But this doesn't mean that activity isn't important. As well as its many other benefits, it has a vital role in helping to keep weight off.

It is worth thinking about what you expect from activity and what you believe it will achieve before starting out with any changes. You can expect the feel-good benefits and the sense of achievement to be immediate, but changes to body shape, weight and fitness will not usually be seen for at least the first 10–12 weeks of regular increased activity.

One of the reasons why activity is advised in combination with changes to eating is because activity changes on their own will result in fairly slow progress with weight loss and shape change. It is very difficult to lose more than about ½ lb every two weeks or so by only changing activity, particularly if you haven't been active for a while and you're building up fitness slowly. Changing only activity habits can be the way forward for some people, however, as long as they can keep motivated to continue. But focusing on the immediate benefits of activity, the "feel-good" factor and the achievement of doing regular activity may help more than thinking only of how much weight has been lost.

"Exercise makes me hungrier"

"I really don't know why I bother exercising. It never helps me lose weight. Swimming is my favourite activity, but when I come out of the pool I'm just so hungry I find it almost impossible to resist getting something from the vending machine. What is the point of going swimming if it is just going to cause me to eat more?"

There is a common belief that exercise increases appetite. However, research has shown that activity has very little effect on physical hunger, except when exercise is done very intensely for long periods, similar to the levels of an athlete. Interestingly, activity *does* seem to influence people's food choices, with those who are regularly active showing a greater tendency to pick healthier foods such as bread and pasta.

But what can the explanation be for this common belief? One suggestion has been that although increased activity doesn't result in a physical trigger to eat more, unless we are exercising at very high levels, it might change the way food choices are thought about. So it might be something along the lines of "I've just swum 30 lengths so I deserve a nice chocolate bar." Sometimes activity can be used as way of giving ourselves permission to eat something more fattening than usual. Of course eating a chocolate bar is fine so long as it's part of the overall plan. However, it can interfere with weight loss if it happens very frequently. Also, if few other food changes have occurred or the plan for losing weight focuses only on changing physical activity, rather than a combination of food and activity, there will be problems. So it is important to be aware of how thinking about food choices can sometimes change as activity increases.

Also, often what we believe to be physical hunger turns out to be food cravings. Chapter 7 gives more details of how to work out the difference between these two feelings and how to cope with cravings.

Sometimes the explanation for strong feelings of physical hunger after activity can be quite practical and might be to do with the timing of meals and snacks. It may be that the activity is done before work, so breakfast might be a bit later than usual, or on the way home from work, so the evening meal is delayed, and hunger levels would therefore naturally be higher than if no activity had been done.

Planning ahead can be particularly helpful in these situations. Taking a healthy snack – something like a banana or yoghurt – that can be eaten straight after the activity can take the edge off hunger until the next meal. This avoids having to grab whatever food is available at the time and this can be really important at times when hunger levels are high. The hungrier you are, the more difficult it can be to make the healthier choice. It can also be helpful to think about having a healthy snack about two hours *before* activity to help prevent post-activity hunger.

How to Do It

"Exercise burns a lot of calories"

Exercise *can* burn lots of calories, but to do so it must be quite intense and quite frequent. This level of exercise is well beyond what most people can manage if they are fairly unfit.

How many calories are burned by being more active will vary from one person to the next, depending on their weight and gender. As a general rule of thumb, though, half an hour of moderate activity will use up about 200–250 calories, depending on the type of activity. So active people like those from the National Weight Control Registry use up about 400 calories a day through physical activity. This may seem like a lot of effort for not many calories worked off, but of course the importance of activity in helping to control weight is about so much more than just how many calories are used up.

It can be quite common for people to believe they are burning off more calories through activity than they really are. This probably doesn't matter unless they use it as part of their decision about food choices. It is common for there to be a mismatch between what someone believes they are working off and what they then decide to eat, for example: "Well, I've just walked for 30 minutes so that will have burned off an extra slice of pizza." Walking for 30 minutes will burn off about 200 calories, whereas a large slice of pizza will be about 400 calories. If mismatches like this one occur regularly it can interfere with managing weight.

Although it's important to be realistic about what can be "burnt off" with activity, this doesn't mean you need to know all the calorific values for foods and activities and make complex calculations throughout the day. But it is helpful to be aware that half an hour of activity does not mean that high-calorie food choices won't count. Equally, it's helpful to be aware that thinking can change as activity increases and this can sometimes result in eating more high-calorie foods than usual, as **Linda's** story illustrates:

> *"I usually drove to work but had recently started to walk and was pleased with how well I was doing. Not once had I taken the car*

in the last month. So I was shocked when I found out my weight had actually increased. My usual reaction to this would have been to give up completely, but I was so determined this time to make things work that I stopped and made myself really think through what had been happening. It took me some time, but I worked out I'd been rewarding myself for all the effort I'd put into walking with extra food. Without really realizing it little thoughts had popped into my head like 'You've been really good with the walking, so it'll be fine to have an extra serving.' They were really brief thoughts, but I reacted to them and ate more than usual. Finding different ways of rewarding myself was essential."

Knowing What to Do

We've looked in detail at some unhelpful approaches to changing activity and taking time to think these through can often be enough for changes to begin to take place. This next section moves on to considering more helpful approaches.

Assessing activity

Working out how active you are at the moment is the first stage of assessing whether this might be an area of your lifestyle to consider changing. It is may be that you decide you are already active enough or you wish to focus on other areas. However completing some sort of assessment can be helpful in coming to this decision.

There are several ways of assessing how active you are. Keeping records of activity as described in Chapter 3 is one very helpful way. The second approach that can be helpful is to use a pedometer. This is a small matchbox-sized device that counts the number of steps you take during the day. It can be worn at the waist by simply clipping it to a belt or the top of trousers or skirts. It should be put on first thing in the morning and taken off last thing at night and will give a reasonably accurate assessment of the amount of walking done during the day.

At the end of each day make a note of the number of steps walked and then after a week compare your average over the week to the categories below. You may be surprised:

Less than 5,000 steps per day – inactive
Between 5,000 and 7,500 – low active
Between 7,500 and 9,999 – somewhat active
More than 10,000 – active
More than 12,500 – very active

Source: Wendy Bumgardner

Once you have an idea which category you fall into, you can begin thinking through ways of increasing the number of steps – unless of course you're already in the "very active" category.

The aim is to work towards increasing the number of steps taken daily by about 2,000. As with all changes, though, it is important to be realistic. You might decide to increase by 500 or 1,000 a day at first. There are no hard and fast rules and it is up to you to work out what is most likely to work well for you. Building up to 10,000 steps per day is the target for weight loss and improved health. This is the equivalent of walking 5 miles, which, if no other changes were made, would result in weight loss in the region of 1 lb each week.

Smaller changes are just as important, however, and all activity will beneficial. Even small changes can make a big difference, as **Kirsty** found:

"When I was first given a pedometer I didn't have a clue what it was for or how to use it. But it was so easy. If someone had asked me before I did this whether I was an active person I think I would have said I was as active as most people I knew. But wearing the pedometer really brought it home to me how inactive I was. On most days I found it hard to clock up more than 3,500 steps, so I was definitely classed as inactive. And when I really thought about my activity it was not surprising. I drove to work and would drive round for ages trying to find the parking spot closest to my build-ing. I sat at a desk all day and took the lift whenever I ventured

out of the office. At the end of the day I'd drive home and then plonk myself in front of the TV feeling completely exhausted.

"But using the pedometer and knowing the figures I needed to aim for was really helpful and motivating. I started with the plan of increasing my steps by 1,000 each day so I could reach about 4,500 steps on most days. I started with a few small changes but was really surprised to see what a difference they made to the number of steps taken:

Parked car further away from building – 300 steps

Took stairs down to lunch (got lift back up) – 100 steps

Took messages to people in my building rather than sent e-mail – 400 steps on busy days

Walked to the local shops or friends' houses during the evening – 300 to 500 steps

"I could see what a difference these four changes could make to the number of steps I was taking each day and they really weren't that hard to do – I just had to keep reminding myself about them, but then the pedometer reading helped me do that."

Pedometers are fairly inexpensive and range from about £7 to £25. They are available in sports shops or can be ordered over the internet. Try the Move4health website (www.move4health. org.uk) that allows online ordering of a good-quality pedometer. As well as being a good way of assessing activity, pedometers are also very useful in helping to keep going with any changes.

What Might Be Stopping You from Being More Active?

If you've assessed how active you are and feel this might be something you want to begin changing it can be helpful to check through what might get in the way of making these changes. This can be particularly helpful if you've tried to be more active before and struggled to keep these changes in place.

Listed below are some of the common reasons that interfere with people being more active. Some of these may be relevant to you, others may not, but the process of thinking through possible barriers to increasing activity is often useful:

- a negative experience of activity
- not feeling confident in your ability to be active
- lack of time
- finding it expensive
- finding it boring
- disappointment with the "results"
- fear of injury or damaging health

The key for many people is finding an activity that is enjoyable. This might sound obvious, but it's often forgotten. If activity is seen as a chore that is only done to lose weight, the chances of continuing it are not good. You may already have an idea of which activities are likely to suit you or you may be unsure and need to try out a few before you find something that suits.

If you feel the barriers listed above are holding you back, here are some ideas that may help you to discover some solutions that are specific to you and your lifestyle.

Negative experiences of activity

It can be helpful to think through why the experience was negative. Was it to do with what you had to wear or where you had to get changed, or did you feel you just weren't good enough at the activity? It may be none of these reasons, but this gives an idea of the kind of questions to think about.

Once you've worked out what puts you off, it's possible to start thinking through other options. So if the competitiveness of some activities is not something you enjoy, you might consider alternatives such as walking, gardening, dancing, water aerobics or yoga. Broadening what is thought of as activity can be useful here. If you feel self-conscious doing some activities, would you feel more comfortable doing others? Would being active with the support of a friend or family member be helpful?

Not feeling confident in your ability to be active

This is often connected to difficult experiences of activity that may have knocked your confidence. It is all too easy to think that if you're not good at one or two activities then you're just no good at exercise in general. Of course this isn't the case. Only a small number of people are naturally good at sport. The majority need a good amount of teaching and lots of practice – something that may not always be encouraged if the skill isn't naturally there.

If there is a skill or a sport that you would really like to take part in, this might be something to consider learning either now or in the future as fitness and self-confidence increase.

If learning about a new activity doesn't appeal, then think of some options that do not involve any particular sporting skill, for example walking, gardening, dancing or vigorous housework. Again, think through options that don't involve "being good" at something or having particular skills but which have all the same benefits for health, weight and well-being.

Lack of time

This is one of the most common barriers to being more active. Moving activity up the priority list in a busy life can be difficult, but it is possible. It isn't necessary to be active all in one go – it can be divided up during the day into 10 or 15-minute sessions that can be easier to fit in. You might want to think through more active ways of doing your usual household jobs or getting from one place to the next.

Fitting activity into a busy life does have the added bonus of helping with the stresses and strains of a hectic schedule by reducing stress and improving mood and sleeping habits. Combining activity with socialising can also be an option if being active with others appeals to you – a day with the family in the park, joining a local walking club or trying a dance class are just a few of the many possibilities.

Finding an option that is convenient is important. If you decide to go swimming a couple of times a week in the evening but find that once you get home it's too tempting to just stay there, consider other times that may be more helpful. Would taking your swimming kit to work and then going to the pool on the way home make it easier or would a swim at lunchtime or first thing in the morning be a better option?

Finding it expensive

Joining a gym or taking up a new sport can be expensive, particularly if lots of equipment is needed. However it isn't necessary to choose these options to gain the benefits of activity. There are a number of activities that cost nothing but provide all the same benefits for your health and weight. Walking is one of the cheapest activities, with the only equipment needed being a good pair of shoes.

Finding it boring

This can be the case if you've chosen an activity you're not really interested in or don't enjoy very much. Of course it is possible to start out doing an activity you enjoy but then lose interest after a while. If you feel this may happen to you it can be helpful to choose a variety of activities to keep up your interest and motivation. Being active with others can be helpful here.

Disappointment with the "results"

As we've already mentioned, expecting increased activity to bring rapid results either with weight change or change in body shape will lead to disappointment. Check that your expectations are realistic at the outset. Focusing on the achievement of being more active rather than on the results that activity will produce is often a more positive approach.

Fear of injury or damaging health

This is an understandable concern, particularly if you haven't been active for a while. If you are worried, and particularly if you have a health problem, it is wise to consult your family doctor before starting. Remember that beginning slowly and building up gradually is important.

How Does It Apply to You?

Having read about the benefits of activity and some of the unhelpful approaches and barriers to being more active, it is useful to stop and think through in detail how all of this applies to you. The following chart will help you to do this.

Benefits of activity for me
_____
_____
_____
_____

What's stopping me being more active?
_____
_____
_____
_____

What would I need to change to be more active?
_____
_____
_____
_____

Which activities might work well for me?
_____
_____
_____
_____

How Much Activity Makes a Difference?

Any increase in activity is better than none. No changes are ever pointless. However, research does give us an idea of how much activity is needed to reduce the chances of ill health, for example heart disease and diabetes, and to maintain weight loss.

It is suggested that 30 minutes of moderate-intensity activity needs to be done on most if not all days of the week to improve health and reduce risk of disease. Moderate-intensity activities are those that make you breathe faster but don't prevent you from talking or leave you gasping for air, for example brisk walking, gardening or vigorous housework. This doesn't have to be done all in one go – two 15-minute sessions during the day will provide the same benefits. So, it is possible to meet the target with three 10-minute walks each day.

Unfortunately in today's society it is very easy to be inactive. Lifts and cars mean we don't need to walk much and washing machines, dish washers and food processors have made many household chores much easier than they were 20 or 30 years ago. Even the weekly shop can be delivered to the door without having to move away from the computer screen. Of course, there is no need to give up these useful advances. However, it does mean that we have to think about how we are going to be more active, as it is often no longer a part of everyday life.

But how much activity is needed to help in controlling weight and keeping weight off once it has been lost? Experts now believe that because our environment has changed so much over recent years, with high-calorie foods so readily available and "super sizing" of portions becoming such a common part of the way we eat, the amount of activity needed to prevent weight regain may need to be about 60 to 90 minutes each day. People who have struggled to control their weight but have then managed to lose weight seem to need to do about an hour of activity each day to keep their weight at the lower level. Again, this doesn't need to be done in one go but can be divided up during the day.

This may sound daunting, particularly if you're fairly inactive at the moment. But as with all changes discussed throughout this book the key is to start slowly, make changes that are realistic and gradually build on those changes over time. Setting short-term targets that are too tough to meet makes it much more likely that you will struggle, become frustrated and give up altogether. So take it gently at first.

Which Activities Are Helpful?

Any activity that involves moving the body more than usual will be beneficial to health and weight. Some of these approaches may surprise you . . .

Cutting down on sedentary activities

Look first at how long you spend doing inactive hobbies like watching TV or sitting at the computer. Some people spend hours watching TV as a way of relaxing. Of course this is fine if other ways of being more active are also part of their lifestyle. But watching too much TV has been linked to problems with weight. Research has suggested that watching two hours of TV regularly each day increases the risk of becoming obese by 23 per cent. Other research in overweight children has shown that cutting back on TV watching and other sedentary behaviour is a very helpful way of increasing activity. If you're not sitting down, then you must be more active, no matter what you are doing.

Again, changing this behaviour is not about making extreme changes – it isn't necessary to ban yourself from ever turning on the TV again. But think through how long you spend watching TV and then consider ways of spending less time doing this. It may be, for example, that you spend some time doing something else – anything else – before you turn the telly on. TVs in bedrooms often make it harder to turn the TV off at night, so it may be worth thinking through where your TV lives in the house and whether it would be helpful to move it.

TV watching can make planned food changes more difficult to cope with too. TV watching is often linked with eating high-calorie snack foods and food cravings are common while watching favourite programmes. TV adverts for various tempting high-calorie foods don't really help with this either. It may also be that whatever we eat while sitting in front of the telly isn't really fully recognised or enjoyed. Many people have experienced a bowl of food "disappearing" whilst they were watching TV. So cutting back on time spent watching TV or doing other sedentary activities not only helps increase overall activity but also makes food changes easier to cope with.

Increasing lifestyle activities

Putting more activity into the way we live our lives can be a really useful way of increasing overall activity. It may not seem as though doing more gardening or washing the kitchen floor vigorously will make much difference to weight, but all of these changes added together really can be helpful.

Here are some changes that people have used as a way of increasing their lifestyle activity:

- Taking several trips upstairs rather than piling things on the stairs for one trip later
- Doing own house-cleaning and gardening
- Taking activity breaks during commercials
- Throwing away the remote control and getting up to change channels
- Taking the dog for walks rather than just letting him loose in the garden
- Parking at the furthest end of the car park and walking to the shops
- Taking the stairs rather than the lift
- Taking activity breaks every hour during the working day
- Taking a 15-minute walk during lunch break
- Getting off the bus a few stops earlier than usual and walking
- Walking to the local shops rather than driving

Think through some of your day-to-day habits and see whether there is any way you could "choose the active option". Using a pedometer to monitor what a difference this can make to activity can be very helpful.

Increasing aerobic activity

Adding aerobic activity to your more active lifestyle will make your heart stronger and more efficient as well as helping with loss of body fat. Jogging, cycling, swimming, dancing, racquet sports like tennis or squash and rowing are all examples of aerobic activities. Aerobic activity should make you breathe harder but you should still be able to talk while you're doing it. If you want to check you're working at the right pace it is possible to measure your heart rate using a monitor and the local leisure centre can often help with this type of fitness assessment.

It's important to begin by establishing a routine. In the first few weeks or months the focus needs to be on getting used to a regular pattern of activity and working out which days and times are going to be best for you. The first time you do your exercise you may manage, say, 10 minutes and then the same again at the second session in the week. You may not feel that this is much and may be tempted to really push yourself at the next session, but this can be off-putting. Simply maintaining your routine (how often you exercise) needs to be the main focus in the early stages. Then, as it becomes more established, you can build on how long you exercise.

It is important to warm up and cool down at the start and the end of aerobic activity to prevent injuries. Warming up helps to raise body temperature and send more blood to the muscles to make sure they work properly and prepares you mentally for the aerobic activity. Warm-up exercises should last for about five minutes and can be something like marching on the spot or power walking to help raise your pulse and get the blood pumping more quickly round the body. A warm up should also include some stretching exercises to lengthen muscles and increase the range of movement. It is important that stretches are done carefully and slowly. If you do not know any stretches, then a trainer at a local leisure centre or gym may be able to help you.

Cooling down after aerobic activity is also important and can help reduce some of the muscle soreness that can occur. Walking or marching on the spot for five minutes brings down the heart rate and breathing, and the pace can be slowed over the five minutes. Stretches at this point can also help reduce muscle soreness as well as keep you strong and flexible. Again, do the stretches carefully and slowly. Pay particular attention to this if you are feeling tired, as this can make you lose attention and overdo it.

Changing activity habits is not easy and it takes time to establish a new routine and to feel comfortable about it. It is often necessary to experiment to work out which activities are most likely to work for you and how best to fit them in to your lifestyle. Remember, if one approach doesn't work that doesn't mean you can't "do" exercise, it just means you need to try an alternative way of being more active.

Summary

- Assess your usual activity rate by keeping records and/or using a pedometer. Both of these will also help keep a track of changes to activity.
- As you plan ways of being more active it can be useful to consider the following questions:
  Do you find it helpful to exercise alone or with other people?
  Do you prefer to be active outdoors, at home or in the gym?
  How much money do you want to spend on being more active?
  What is the most convenient time of the day to be more active?
- Start slowly and set goals that are realistic. For example if you've decided to walk more and are using a pedometer, set a daily increase of 500–1,000 steps (or less than this if 500 steps sounds too unmanageable). It doesn't matter

where you start from, so long as you build up from this point and keep going.

- If you haven't been active for a while, think about cutting down on sedentary activities and increasing lifestyle activities first to help build up fitness levels before starting on aerobic activities.
- Choose activities that you enjoy and feel comfortable with. Activities that make you feel self-conscious or vulnerable are going to be very hard to keep up.
- Be aware of how tempting it can be to reward increased activity with higher-calorie food.
- With aerobic activity, establish your routine first before you begin building on how long or how hard you are working.
- Check you have appropriate clothing and sports shoes. Drinking plenty of water routinely is essential to prevent dehydration. Over a day our bodies need about six to eight glasses of fluid. When we are active we need extra water, particularly if activity makes you sweat. Water is the healthiest choice and unless you're doing very large amounts of activity sports drinks aren't necessary. Try to take sips of water before and during activity and drink at least a couple of glasses of water afterwards.
- Boredom is one of the most common reasons that people give up on activity, so choose activities you get something positive from, whether that's a feeling of well-being or a skill you enjoy practising. Doing a variety of different activities is also helpful.
- Focus on the achievement of being more active rather than the eventual results of the activity.

5

Changing Eating Habits

"I go for just one night out and by the next morning I've gained 3lb."
"Dieting is pointless. It doesn't work."

Many people, particularly, dieting "veterans" may already feel they know how they should eat to lose weight. However, unreliable information about managing weight is all around us, and many people have developed attitudes and approaches to changing eating that are often unhelpful and limit chances of success. So the first section of this chapter explores the truth behind commonly held food and dieting beliefs and the impact these may have on your likelihood of success at losing weight. It may be tempting to skip this section, particularly if you've followed diets before and feel you have a good knowledge already. However, checking out your facts is a really important first stage in deciding the best way forward.

This chapter is not about providing you with lists of suggested food changes or eating plans – there are already a number of books on the market that do that job very well (and some that do it very badly) – but to try and put you in the best possible position to make a truly informed choice about which approach to changing your eating is likely to be the most successful for you.

Information presented in this chapter is in line with current medical and dietetic research and practice at the time of going to print.

Unhelpful Dieting Beliefs

"If only I could find the right diet . . ."

There is a common belief that successful weight loss is solely dependent on finding the right diet. We have already seen how unhelpful this can be. The result can be simply frustration, self-blame and guilt. Rather than searching for yet another diet, it would be of greater benefit to learn how to cope with the inevitable challenges that will be part of any attempt to change eating behaviour. More on this in the following chapters.

"Dieting is pointless. It doesn't work"

Frustration with dieting is a very understandable outcome of struggling to control weight and can lead to the belief that it's pointless. However, this statement is really quite misleading and it would be more accurate to say:

- Changing eating habits is hard to keep up.
- Quick-fix extreme diets are not helpful.

Science has shown that diets work for as long as we can keep them going. That's why extreme or fad diets that require people to make very severe changes to the way they eat are usually impossible to sustain. So the challenge is not about looking for an alternative treatment to dieting but understanding more about what helps people sustain changes to their eating (and activity).

Only recently has "maintenance" of changed behaviour and weight been recognized as an important issue. Traditionally people are encouraged to just think about losing weight. It now seems that thinking through whether the changes you choose for weight loss can be continued in the long term might be much more important than initially realized.

One key factor in sustaining changes to eating seems to be ensuring that the initial food changes are realistic. The question to ask yourself is: "Can I see myself continuing with this change one to two years down the line?" The next chapter deals in more detail with making changes work.

Of course, there are other weight-loss treatments apart from dieting. Medication and surgery can be accessed through general practitioners and specialist obesity clinics. They will discussed more in Chapter 9. Yet these treatments aren't used in isolation but are considered additional to changes to eating and activity, not a replacement for such changes.

"I go for just one night out and by the next morning I've gained 3lb"

A weight increase after a night out can be devastating. Often it can lead someone to abandon attempts to change eating patterns. Usually, though, it is not the amount or type of food that has been eaten that leads to weight gain but people's reactions to eating more than they had planned. Many people have been on a night out, eaten and drunk more than planned and then thought, "Well, I've blown it now, so I might as well really go overboard."

Chapter 9 explains how to deal differently with these situations. The message here is to try and keep such events in perspective. It is useful to bear in mind that what is done on a day-to-day basis is more important than what is eaten or drunk on the odd night out.

You may well be wondering how someone could see a 3lb weight increase if all they had done was have a beer and a curry. Body weight is not just a measure of body fat but of all the components within the body such as bone, muscle, liver, kidneys and fluid. Rapid rises in weight will most likely be due to increases in fluid that will resolve in time. It can be quite common for women to retain fluid around the time of menstruation, for example. (Under no circumstances should fluid intake be restricted in an attempt to lose weight, as this will simply result in the body becoming dehydrated and have no effect on body fat.)

So it is important to recognize that *what the scales tell you doesn't always mean what you think it does*. A person's weight goes up and down quite naturally during the day and from one day to the next for all sorts of reasons, including hormonal and fluid changes, bowel changes and the type of food and drink consumed.

For this reason, many people find weighing themselves every day too confusing. It is difficult not to react negatively if you see a rapid rise in numbers. If this sounds like you, it may well be helpful to weigh yourself only once a week, or even once a month. However there are no rigid rules and it's about working out what is most helpful to you. Some people find weighing themselves more regularly than once a week is really important in keeping them "on track".

"Salad is good for you, chocolate is bad"

Salad is certainly part of a healthy way of eating, but chocolate can be too. Labelling foods with moral words such as "good" or "bad" or "naughty" or "nice" is common in the media and in popular weight-loss diets — so common in fact that it can be a challenge to stop. However, it is important to think through what effect this habit can have on your eating and the way you feel about yourself.

Believing a certain kind of food is "naughty" tends to make us want to eat it more but to feel guilty for doing so. Not only does this tend to remove our enjoyment of the food but it can lead to the "Well, I've blown it now so I might as well just continue" effect. The opposite can be true for food that we think is good for us. How many times have you heard someone say "I really don't like it, but I know it's good for me so I'm going to eat it"? This belief about "good" food tends to make it less appealing and result in people feeling they "should" eat it. As we saw in Chapter 1, "shoulds" do not seem to work for motivation in the long term. Of course, some food is healthier than other food and can be eaten in larger amounts and more often. However, the overall habit of labelling is still not helpful.

It is far better to consider food for what it really is. So chocolate is high-fat food that can be included sometimes and salad is healthy food that can be (if you like it) included regularly. The important point is that *all* food can be part of a healthy way of eating.

Working towards developing a more positive attitude to all food can have long-term benefits. If you do think of certain types of food as "bad", it is important to try and remove these labels and give yourself permission to include the food in your diet (*see Chapter 2 for more details of changing thinking*). Successfully removing labels can help take away guilt and ultimately improve your enjoyment of eating.

"As long as everything I buy is fat free, weight will drop off"

Fat-free foods are often believed to be calorie free, but changing over to fat-free products alone may not lead to the weight loss you might expect.

There are two main reasons for this. The first is that fat-free, reduced-fat or low-fat products are not always the low-calorie choices we believe them to be. Secondly, there can be a tendency to increase the amount we eat because we think our food is calorie free. Have you ever bought a packet of reduced-fat biscuits or cake, had one piece and then thought, "Oh I'll just treat myself to another one. They are low fat, after all."

Reading food labels is important for many manufactured foods – even those you may think will have little or no fat can sometimes be surprisingly high in "hidden" fat. There is more on understanding food labels later in this chapter.

"If I skip a meal, that's a good start"

Sandra had been on and off various quick-fix diets for most of her adult life. Over the years she had got into the habit of skipping meals during the day. When she first started to do this it had seemed like a good way to lose weight. She regularly felt tired, a bit dizzy and irritable during the middle of the morning or late afternoon, but she never thought this might be linked to her lack of food. Eventually she got so used to ignoring her body's hunger signals during the day that she no longer wanted to eat until evening. Despite all of this her weight hadn't fallen at all, but had risen to its highest point ever.

Although it seems logical to think that severely restricting food during the day or going for long periods without eating will lead to weight loss, an eating pattern like Sandra's is often linked with difficulty controlling weight. In Sandra's case by the time she got home she was so hungry that once she started eating she felt the need to continue throughout the evening. Also, allowing herself to become "over hungry" had made it more difficult to control food choices and portion sizes. She tended to think, "Well, I've had a hard day and I've eaten nothing at all, so I deserve a couple of extra biscuits. And another spoon of lasagne won't do any harm."

Once Sandra had got used to the idea that she needed to spread her food out more evenly during the day she felt in more control during the evening. She was more able to make the kind of healthy choices that she had planned and was less inclined to pick and snack than previously. It took some practice. At first she felt as though she was eating when she wasn't hungry, but over time her hunger signals returned and rather than feeling scared of them she began to respond and to eat when she felt hungry.

There are no hard and fast rules about when to eat and it isn't necessary to stick to any rigid timetable for meals or snacks. You can eat at whatever time suits you and your lifestyle. It is a myth that eating late at night leads to greater weight gain than if the same food was consumed earlier in the day. It is the number of calories eaten *throughout the day* compared to the number used up through activity that affects weight and body fat.

For most people though it is wise to eat regularly, usually three times a day at least. Long periods without food will cause blood sugar levels to fall and that can cause light-headedness, irritability and tiredness. Eating regularly keeps the blood sugar level stable, preventing these unpleasant feelings, and makes healthier choices more likely.

More Helpful Beliefs

Here are some more positive – and accurate – alternatives to the unhelpful beliefs above:

- Finding a way of eating that suits you is only one part of understanding how best to manage your weight.
- Changing your eating habits is an important part of managing weight but changes must be realistic and sustainable.
- Large increases in body fat do not occur overnight or after one night out.
- Weight will only be lost when energy from food is less than energy used through activity. (This is not saying weight loss is simple!)
- Labelling foods with positive and negative tags tends to lead to problematic attitudes to food and managing weight.
- Eating at regular intervals throughout the day is often helpful in managing weight.
- A good understanding of how to read food labels can be useful.

How Weight is Controlled

"I just don't understand why I can't lose weight – I eat next to nothing and yet still gain weight."

"I can only lose about a stone and then my weight loss just stops. There's something wrong with my metabolism."

These are common experiences and beliefs among people trying to manage weight. In order to understand what's going on it can be helpful to understand more about how the body controls weight.

The basics of energy balance

The control of weight is a balancing act between the amount of energy (calories) you take in from food and the amount you work off through physical activity. When you are "in balance", the energy that you're eating equals that burned off through activity and your weight will remain the same. Only when your body goes "out of balance" can you lose or gain weight.

Imagine a plastic container that can either shrink or expand depending on how much is stored inside it. At the top of the container is a water tap and at the bottom an outflow tap. When water is run into the container at the same rate as it flows out of the tap at the bottom, the container stays the same size. Only if less water goes into the container than is running out will it shrink (and vice versa).

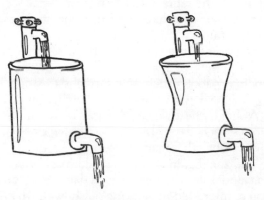

Now imagine the container is your body, the water flowing in is food and that flowing out is activity. Body weight will only be lost when fewer calories from food flow in than go out as activity.

This is probably something you've heard many times before and it may not seem a particularly helpful statement. It does tend to make weight loss sound simple – just eat less and exercise more. What it tends not to highlight are the many complicated factors and systems that influence what and why people eat and how active they are.

Nevertheless, understanding the basics of energy balance can be helpful when things don't go to plan. If weight loss isn't happening it's because either because too many calories are being eaten or not enough are being used up, or most likely a combination of both these. This is a situation where recording eating and activity (*see Chapter 3*) would be particularly beneficial in helping to pinpoint where changes may have slipped a little.

"My husband never puts on weight. It's not fair"

Sandra couldn't understand why she struggled so much with her weight. At work she would be the person with salad and cottage cheese on her plate while others piled on the chips and fried food. It was the same with her husband – he seemed to be able to eat whatever he liked and not put on an ounce. Life seemed very unfair.

Comparing your eating patterns to those of other people isn't helpful for a variety of reasons. Let's take Sandra's situation again. Sandra is 5 foot 3 inches and weighs 13 stone, but wants to get her weight down to what she weighed five years ago – 11 stone. At her current weight Sandra's body will use up about 2,000 calories each day. This means if she eats roughly this amount her weight will remain stable, any less and she'll lose and any more and she'll gain. Sandra would lose weight if she ate about 500 calories less than usual each day (i.e. 1,500 calories a day). If you're interested in working out how much energy your body uses up each day, look at www.dallasdietitian.com, where you can calculate your individual needs.

So are there any differences between one person's body and another's in terms of their energy needs? There certainly are, depending on how much someone weighs, the amount of muscle they have and how active they are. The higher their weight, muscle and activity, the more calories they will burn off each day. This is contrary to the popular belief that a slow metabolism can be a cause of being overweight. Science has shown that the *higher someone's weight, the higher their metabolic rate*. Sandra's husband is 15½ stone and his body uses up 2,700 calories a day, so he can eat about 700 calories more than Sandra before he's at the point where he may gain weight. This is part of the explanation why he manages to eat more and not gain weight.

One of the key difficulties in Sandra comparing herself to other people is that in most instances she only gets a snapshot of what someone is eating throughout the day, even her husband. She may see what they eat at one meal and compare that to what she is eating, but this is often not an accurate reflection of the total amount they have eaten during the day. It is certainly not detailed enough to understand what their average intake is over a number of days or weeks. It's also very important to factor in how active someone is and this can also be very difficult to judge accurately.

Probably the most important reason for Sandra not comparing herself with others is it doesn't get her any further ahead in managing her own weight but will most likely just add to her frustration and lead her down the path of thinking there is something medically "wrong". What is more likely to be helpful is for her to focus on the factors that she does have some control over: her food and activity choices. Sandra needs to revisit the basics of energy balance. If she's not losing weight then the energy from her food must be higher than the amount *her* body is using. Keeping detailed records of eating and activity habits would be an excellent way to discover what might be preventing weight loss in such a situation.

What if weight loss has been going well and then suddenly it slows and eventually stops?

There are a number of possible explanations for this, depending on how much weight has been lost. If weight has fallen substantially, by about 15–20lb, then a readjustment to eating and/or activity may be needed. This is because as weight falls not only is body fat lost but so is a small amount of muscle, and it is the amount of muscle in the body that is important in determining metabolism. So as you lose weight, you lose muscle, your metabolism drops and your now smaller body needs less energy each day. However this is not a big effect. Most people need to reduce their food intake by another 200 calories per day to restart weight loss.

If only small amounts of weight have been lost weight before progress slows and then stops, the explanation will lie in alterations in eating and activity rather than in any kind of fault with metabolism. When a person begins to make changes, they start off by concentrating on the task and prioritising it. However, over time it is human nature for such changes not to remain at the forefront of the mind and as they become a lower priority, they may begin to slip.

Jackie's experience of this is very typical. At first everything had gone well. She'd bought a steamer and changed how her food was cooked and had been really careful with the portions she served herself. Swimming was probably the only activity she really enjoyed, so she'd started going back to the local pool three times a week with a friend from work. The weight was definitely coming off and she was delighted. But then disaster struck. As she weighed herself on week 6 she had gained ½ lb (0.2 kg). It just didn't make sense! "What was the point of all that work?" she thought. "I might just as well go back to what I was doing before and at least enjoy myself." By the end of the day she'd returned to her old ways of eating.

The key in situations like this is to develop the detective skills to be able to work out where the slips may have occurred and why (*see Chapter 3 for a more detailed discussion*). It is not always obvious. A number of very subtle changes can make all the difference between losing or gaining weight. In Jackie's case, without realizing it she had become almost a little too confident about the weight loss and had tended to think: "It's all going well so a little bit extra of this won't do any harm." As this happened, her portion sizes and snacking had crept up. She worked this out by keeping detailed records of her eating behaviour and thinking through exactly what had happened.

Helpful Approaches

We have looked in detail at some of the common food beliefs that are usually unhelpful in making positive changes to eating. Taking time to think through unhelpful beliefs can often be enough for changes to begin to take place. This next section moves on to consider more helpful approaches.

The first step is to try and see if anything can be learned from past experience of dieting. (If you've never tried to change your diet before, please move on to the next section, A Review of Popular Diets, page 112.)

In order to learn from past dieting experience it is important to take time to think through which diets you've tried before and whether any of these were more or less successful than the others. It is also useful to consider other factors that may have played a part in your ability to keep dietary changes in place. See if **Sandra's** experience of dieting throws any light on this process.

Which diet	When	Outcome	What interfered?/ Life events	Learned anything?
Cambridge diet	Age 23	Lost 3 stone in 3 months but quickly regained.	Sitting university exams. Snacking when stressed. Difficult to limit alcohol.	Eating in response to stress is a problem.
Weight Watchers	Age 27	Lost 4 stone over 1 year. Gradual regain over next 2 years.	Motivation was fitting into wedding dress. Started new job after honeymoon and weight was less of a priority.	Group support helped keep me on track. Lost my way a bit when new job started – was stressed and eating out was a regular part of the job.

Which diet	When	Outcome	What interfered?/ Life events	Learned anything?
Cabbage soup diet	Age 32	Lost 8lb in 1 week. Had regained 15lb 1 month later.	Struggling to adjust to life at home with a young child. A lot of snacking.	Felt very low about self when weight quickly returned.
Atkins diet	Age 33	3.5kg in 2 days. Regained 4.5kg within 2 weeks.	Gave up. Went to a wedding, friend's birthday and university reunion all in 1 week – disaster – dieting abandoned.	Really struggled to cope with the restriction of doing this one. Felt low.
Slimming World	Age 34	1 stone. Gradual regain when stopped going.	All was going well until I was offered a seat on a bus by a man that thought I was pregnant. I wasn't!	People say hurtful things!

It took Sandra a while to complete this chart (this is only a small section) and at the beginning she really couldn't see the point of doing it. But as she began to think through all her experiences, to record what had been happening at the same time and what she thought she'd learned, she began to recognize patterns to her dieting.

What would you conclude from her chart? You could say that she had tried many different diets, she seemed to lose weight with all of them to varying different degrees but the weight was usually regained. Of course, this is not saying anything surprising and if you just looked at this superficially you could conclude that dieting hadn't worked for her and was pointless. However, looking in more detail gives more information.

Did any of the diets seem to suit her better than others? Let's just look in a bit more detail at her most successful attempt. This was achieved by attending Weight Watchers, where she lost 4 stone before her wedding day. However, it is not clear whether this success was due to the diet alone or to the very strong reason she had for making those changes. In reality it was most likely a combination of these factors. She believed that the regular support with this approach had been helpful in keeping her on track and she did manage to sustain her eating changes for one year. This might be an approach to consider using again in the future. Likewise with Slimming World she had been progressing well until a particularly hurtful comment had thrown her off track.

It is interesting to look at what seems to interfere with her weight-loss attempts. In some instances the diet she had chosen didn't seem to suit her. She found the Atkins diet too restrict-ive and only managed a few days; similarly, she managed the Cabbage Soup diet for about a week. Increased eating in response to stressful situations is mentioned a number of times. Although Sandra did recognize this before completing the chart, taking the time to really think through her past experi-ences helped her to see how important stress was in preventing her succeeding in the longer term. Sandra is now in a better position to consider which dietary approaches to consider for the future, but more importantly is aware of the areas that she needs to focus on changing i.e. coping with emotions and stress in other ways (*see Chapter 7*) and ensuring she has good support to help her through some of the more challenging times.

Although your situation will be different from Sandra's, the principles are the same:

- Take time to think through what you've done before.
- Try to work out what helped and what didn't help.
- Don't just focus on the "type" of diet you chose but think through other areas of your life – they are often just as important.

- Try to work out what made it difficult to continue – feelings, situations, practical difficulties.

This process will hopefully help you to pinpoint not only the types of diets that are more likely to be helpful to you but also the factors that are helping and hindering you in making changes over the long term.

A Review of Popular Diets

You only need to look at the bestseller lists to know that there's no shortage of diets to choose from. However, the multi-million dollar question is: "Which one works best?"

Of course, we know that managing your weight is about much more than simply finding the "right" diet. However, it is true that there are likely to be approaches to changing your eating that will work better for you than others, and there are certainly diets that are better for your health. So which would you choose?

One of the most useful things to do first of all is to separate the extreme faddy diets from the more sensible approaches.

How to spot a fad diet

All of the below are warning signals that a diet is unlikely to be helpful. As a general rule of thumb if something sounds too good to be true then it most likely is.

- any diet that promises weight loss will be quick, easy and painless – we know it isn't
- diets that claim to remove body fat through "detoxification"
- diets that focus on just one or two foods – e.g. the grapefruit diet or the cabbage soup diet
- lists of "good" and "bad" foods
- whole food groups removed or very restricted
- diets that include foods that "melt away body fat" or "raise metabolism"

- diets that state foods have to be eaten in specific combinations
- diets that suggest weight can be managed without changes to activity or lifestyle
- rigid inflexible food choices and meal plans

Unfortunately many of these diets are very cleverly marketed so they sound incredibly appealing. They seem to be the answer to people's prayers – a quick, easy, permanent solution to weight. For most people, though, they offer little long-term hope of managing their weight more effectively. Beware fad diets. No matter how tempting they may sound, avoid travelling down this much beaten but unhelpful track.

Safe and healthy diets

Reviewed below are some of the nutritionally sound dietary treatments that are considered to be safe and healthy. These may be helpful. But remember the diet itself does not hold the secret to success. It is only one piece of the jigsaw and to complete the picture it's essential to understand more about the factors that help or hinder you from putting these changes into practice.

Low fat

- **Examples:** *Cut the Fat* (American Dietetic Association), *American Heart Association Low Fat Cookbook*, *Healthy Eating: Low Fat* (Mary Coleman).
- **What are they?** Most low-fat diets will suggest modest reductions in the amount of fat eaten, with an emphasis on restricting the animal sources of fat (fatty meats, butter, cheese) and replacing them with healthier alternatives (fish, poultry, low-fat spread, reduced-fat cheeses). There are some very low-fat diets (e.g. *Eat More Weigh Less*, Dean Ornish) that suggest such severe restrictions to fat intake that some people find them hard to cope with. In reality it isn't necessary to make massive restrictions to the amount of fat eaten. A number of modest changes can make a big difference to weight over the long term.

- **Do they work?** Restricting fat intake is one of the best ways of limiting energy intake. There is good evidence that following a low-fat way of eating is a helpful treatment not just in managing weight but also in reducing the risk of various diseases that are linked to how we live our lives, such as heart disease and diabetes.
- **Are they safe?** Yes there is nothing to suggest that this approach is unsafe.

Low glycaemic index or low GI diets
- **Examples:** *The GI Point Diet, Living the GI Diet, The Good Carb Diet Plan* and *The New Glucose Revolution*.
- **What are they?** Glycaemic index is a way of ranking carbohydrate foods (bread and cereals) according to their effect on blood sugar level in the body. The theory is that foods which affect blood sugar level quickly (high GI foods) lead to a rapid return of hunger, whereas those that have a more steadying effect (low GI foods) help us to feel fuller for longer. In other words this is a diet that should help avoid large swings in blood sugar and hunger levels. Refined starchy foods such as white bread, rice and cereals are high GI foods, whereas wholegrain breads and pastas, barley and pulses are low GI.
- **Do they work?** The jury is still out on just how helpful this type of diet is for weight loss, but it is a way of eating that contains many healthy foods (fruit, wholegrains and pulses) that protect against heart disease and diabetes. Combining a low glycaemic way of eating with changes to the amount and type of fat eaten is likely to be a helpful way of managing weight and health.
- **Are they safe?** Yes, there is nothing to suggest that this isn't a safe type of diet to follow.

Commercial weight-management groups
- **Examples:** Weight Watchers, Rosemary Conley Diet & Fitness, Slimming World.
- **What are they?** Lay groups often run by people who have had a weight problem themselves but have successfully

managed to lose weight using the commercial group they become the leader for. They provide structure, education, skills and very importantly support from other people in similar situations. The support aspect of these groups is probably one of their most helpful features, although they don't suit everyone.

- **Do they work?** It is very difficult to say exactly how successful these approaches are, as very little research has explored their effectiveness. However, the majority are based on sound principles for managing weight.
- **Are they safe?** Yes. There is nothing to suggest that these approaches are unsafe.

Meal replacements

- **Examples:** Slimfast, Tesco's Ultra Slim, Boots Shapers.
- **What are they?** Ready-portioned shakes, soups, bars and meals that can be used to replace two meals (and snacks) during the day with one healthy main meal of about 600 calories each day. Fruit, vegetables and increased intake of water are encouraged.
- **Do they work?** It's unclear how helpful this approach is if the products are just bought off the shelf and used without any outside help or support. In settings where people have been supported this seems to be a promising approach, with weight loss being maintained over long periods, particularly if one shake (or bar or soup) is used each day to help keep weight off once lost. Some meal replacement companies do provide educational materials and internet support.
- **Are they safe?** Yes. There is nothing in any of the research to suggest that people are at risk from using this approach.

What about very low-calorie diets?

- **Examples:** Cambridge Health Plan, Medifast.
- **What are they?** Usually liquid diets that replace all meals and snacks and severely restrict calorie intake to less than 800 calories a day. They are used for only short periods of

time and should not be used as the only form of treatment but in conjunction with counselling or medical treatment. Very low-calorie diets should not to be undertaken lightly; they are associated with various side-effects and risks and people need to be monitored by their doctor.

- **Do they work?** For most people they work in the short term, but if no additional treatment is used, once the diet stops weight may be regained. However, for some people with serious weight problems they can be a useful start.
- **Are they safe?** There are side-effects and risks and these should be considered carefully with your doctor.

What about low-carbohydrate high-protein diets?

These are incredibly popular diets and there has been much discussion in the media about this approach. However, are these diets an effective way of managing weight and are they safe?

- **Examples:** Dr Atkins New Diet Revolution, The Carbohydrate Addicts Diet, Protein Power, Sugar Busters.
- **What are they?** All these diets require people to cope with extreme restrictions to carbohydrates (bread, potato, rice, past, cereals, even fruit and some vegetables), encourage people to eat large amounts of protein (meat and cheese) and are often high in fat, particularly animal fats. Vitamin and mineral supplements are needed.
- **Does they work?** Although these diets may seem to work better than a low-fat approach in the first few months, by one year there is no difference between their results and those achieved with a low-fat diet.
- **Are they safe?** It is unknown whether this way of eating is safe beyond a 6–12 month period. There has been very little research that has looked at the possible health concerns linked with this type of diet. Many doctors and dietitians are concerned about its possible effect on the kidneys, liver and bones and on the risk of heart disease, diabetes and cancer.

The theory behind low-carbohydrate diets sounds convincing, but in reality the reason why people lose weight with this type of diet is because their intake of energy is lower than usual. No myth, no magical scientific reason – just plain old calorie restriction. Despite all the media hype over this dietary approach, until we have a much greater understanding about it and its potential effects on health it seems unwise to use what is in essence an untested treatment.

The Principles of Eating Well

There is no single approach to changing eating that suits everyone. It is often a matter of experimenting to work out which is most likely to work for you. You might try out any of the safe and healthy dietary treatments above or might prefer to use your own self-styled approach.

Whatever you choose, it isn't essential to try and make all of the changes all of the time. It isn't necessary and often it isn't helpful to try and achieve the "perfect" way of eating. Modest changes sustained over time will lead to weight loss.

Here are some of the important principles to consider in choosing specific food changes.

Plenty of fruit and vegetables

Fruit and vegetables are packed full of vitamins and minerals that we know are important in preventing a whole range of diseases including heart disease, cancer and diabetes. But apart from their general importance in improving and protecting health, they are helpful with weight loss. They are naturally low-fat foods with lots of nutrition and bulk and very few calories. So if the portion of vegetables on your plate increases while the portion of meat, for example, decreases, then you'll have reduced the calories eaten without having to eat any less. This is important, as cutting down too much on all food can leave you feeling physically hungry shortly after a meal and make weight management more difficult.

The plate above shows a healthy balance of food choices, with about half of it filled with vegetables, a quarter with starches like potatoes or rice or pasta and a quarter with protein such as meat, chicken or fish.

If you want more details of what "plenty" of fruit and vegetables means in practice check out the table below. To improve our health and reduce risk of various diseases at least five portions of fruit and vegetables a day is recommended. The more varied your choice of fruit and vegetables, the more likely you are to get a wide range of all the vitamins and minerals and gain more health benefits. In general the more brightly coloured and darker the fruit and vegetable, the higher the number of the protective nutrients it contains – try a mixture of bright red, yellow, orange and dark green fruit and vegetables.

A portion of fruit or vegetables for an adult is about 80g. Here is a rough guide to one portion:

Vegetables – raw, cooked, frozen or tinned: 3 heaped tablespoons
Salad: 1 dessert bowlful
Grapefruit/avocado: ½ fruit
Apple, banana, orange and other similar-sized fruit: 1 fruit
Plums and similar-sized fruit: 2 fruit
Grapes, cherries and berries: 1 cupful
Fruit salad, fresh, stewed or tinned fruit in fruit juice: 3 heaped
    tablespoons

Dried fruit (raisins, apricots, etc.): ½–1 heaped tablespoon
Fruit juice: 1 glass (150 ml)

Remember that:

- Potatoes don't count as a vegetable because they're classed as a starchy carbohydrate (with bread and other cereals).
- Fruit juice counts as a maximum of one portion a day.
- Beans and pulses only count as a maximum of one portion a day, however much you eat.

Adapted from the Food Standards Agency

If you've been keeping a record of your eating habits you'll be aware of roughly how often you eat fruit and vegetables. If you eat very few at the moment, increasing to five portions a day might be a bit unrealistic at first and difficult to sustain. You may want to set more realistic short-term targets such as eating one portion of vegetables and one portion of fruit every day and then building up gradually from there. Of course, if you are already eating five portions and want to increase further, then this is fine. In many Mediterranean countries it is common to eat about eight to nine portions of fruit and vegetables a day. However, it is wise to be careful about the amount of fruit juice drunk in a day. Litres of fruit juice can provide quite a lot of natural sugars (calories) without the bulk and fibre that the fruit itself provides.

If you choose to increase your intake of fruit and vegetables, then you also need to be specific about exactly how you might do this. In other words, what would be the best, most enjoyable and realistic way? Below are some examples of what people have done to increase fruit and vegetables in their diet. Some of these suggestions might sound promising to you, others may not. You will probably be able to come up with some inventive ideas of your own.

Examples of what others have tried and found helpful
- Adding bananas, kiwi fruit, grapes or strawberries to breakfast cereal

- Having a salad before or with a main meal – try cherry tomatoes, sliced peppers, beans and a healthy dressing or a carrot and raisin salad
- Keeping a bowl of fruit on the desk at work
- Having a glass of fruit juice with breakfast
- Adding extra vegetables or pulses to soups, stews and casseroles
- Chopping fruit like bananas or berries into yoghurt or jelly
- Making fruit smoothies with yoghurt
- Adding salad vegetables to sandwiches
- Eating vegetables like carrots, cucumber and cherry tomatoes with low-fat dips
- Having small packets of raisins as snacks

Linda had always said she hated fruit and vegetables, thought they were a hassle to prepare and that they went off before she got round to using them. But once she had decided that she wanted to work on increasing the limited number and range she did like to eat, she made a specific plan. She'd buy a bag of frozen peas, sweetcorn and broccoli at the supermarket every other week, a stock of tinned vegetables for when her supplies ran low and at least one fresh vegetable each week. Sometimes this was one of her favourites like parsnips, but at other times she would buy something new and different – purple sprouting broccoli became a favourite, as did mange tout. Whatever fresh vegetables she had bought would be used first before they went off. She made a decision that the focus would be on two main changes: to include at least one portion of vegetables with her evening meal and to have a glass of fruit juice with breakfast each day. On some days it didn't quite work out, but on many days it did, and it was easier than she'd imagined. At first she thought that the vegetables would take ages to prepare, but she experimented with microwaving and steaming them and it proved quick and easy.

Linda's story is a good example of how keeping changes realistic and thinking through the obstacles can really help improve eating habits.

Plenty of wholegrains

Wholegrains are the healthiest types of cereal and bread. Eating enough of them is important in improving health and helping with weight loss. But what exactly are wholegrains?

There are a wide variety of grains, including rye, wheat, rice, barley, corn and oats. What happens to these grains during processing determines whether they are a wholegrain high-fibre food, sometimes called an unrefined carbohydrate, or a refined food. Many of the protective vitamins and minerals are found in the outer part of the grain and the more refining that occurs, the fewer that are left. For example wholewheat is milled to produce wholemeal flour which, if processed, further produces white flour. Wholemeal and wholegrains are very similar in their nutritional content, while white flour or refined cereal contains far fewer of the protective vitamins and minerals.

Eating plenty of high-fibre wholegrain foods helps protect against a whole range of diseases including cancer and heart disease as well as helping to keep the gut healthy. These foods add bulk without lots of calories and may help to keep people feeling fuller for longer.

Despite popular myth, these foods are not fattening. Research shows they are an important part of a healthy way of eating and should be included at each mealtime. It is wise to consider how they are prepared and cooked, though, as this can be a source of extra fat. For example it is often the creamy or cheesy sauces served with pasta or rice or the oil used to fry potatoes that is fattening, rather than the bread or cereals themselves. The plate model shows the proportion of these foods that can make up a healthy meal.

Wholegrain foods include:

- wholemeal or wholegrain bread or crispbread
- dark seedy breads
- wholewheat breakfast cereals, rolled oats
- wheatgerm
- wholemeal pasta

- brown rice, rice cakes
- puffed wholegrains
- bulgar
- couscous
- popcorn

How much is "plenty"?

How much cereal and bread to include in your diet will vary from person to person, but a good guide is at least four servings per day and usually between six and eight per day. If you want to find out more detail on your individual needs, check out www.bdaweightwise.com. A serving would normally be counted as one slice of bread, three pieces of crispbread, a bowl of breakfast cereal or one cup of rice or pasta. For more details check out www.bdaweightwise.com.

Breakfast and snack times are often good opportunities to increase the number of wholegrains eaten. You might like to try wholegrain or high-fibre breakfast cereal, porridge, wholegrain toast or muffins for breakfast or low-fat popcorn, muesli sprinkled over yoghurt or wholemeal crispbreads or crackers for snacks. Some of these ideas may appeal while others may not. The important point is to experiment and find what works for you.

Although wholegrain foods are a healthier option than refined bread and cereals, that doesn't mean white bread, pasta and rice are unhealthy foods and should not be eaten. As with all food changes, it is a matter of trying to make better choices than usual, not trying to follow the perfect diet. It may be that you love white bread and couldn't enjoy wholemeal bread on a regular basis. In this case swapping a sugar-coated breakfast cereal for porridge, branflakes or Weetabix might be a better alternative to increase the amount of wholegrains eaten.

Limit fatty foods

Fat plays an important role in our bodies and is not the "demon" it is sometimes portrayed as. However, eating too much fat increases the chance of gaining weight and limiting it is usually one of the key changes to consider in managing weight.

There are a number of reasons why fat seems to play such an important role in weight control:

- Fat doesn't fill us up very well. It is a very rich source of calories and the body seems to have a poor natural ability to control how much high-fat food we eat. We tend to eat a set amount of food each day, so if that food is high in fat we will get far more calories than if it were high in starchy carbohydrates. This is sometimes part of the explanation why people may be struggling to control weight and yet not eating large quantities of food – the food they are eating may be high in fat (which is not always obvious) and therefore concentrated in energy.
- Fat is stored by the body very easily and efficiently, more so than protein or carbohydrates.
- Fat certainly adds taste to the food we eat and this makes it easier to eat more of it without necessarily realizing it.
- Very importantly, a high-fat way of eating that includes large amounts of animal or saturated fats such as fatty meats, high-fat dairy foods, fried foods and butter is linked with increased risk of heart disease and cancer.

Swapping some high-fat foods for lower-fat alternatives is often a useful way of cutting down on fat. There are no hard and fast rules about this and you don't have to buy low-fat everything (although you can if this suits you) or deprive yourself of high-fat favourites. High-fat food can still be eaten as part of a healthy diet, but needs to be eaten with an awareness of how much is consumed.

So it is important to be aware of which types of food contains high amounts of fat. Sometime this is obvious, sometimes not. These are some of the high-fat food choices to think through:

- fatty meats – the obvious fat on the outside can be trimmed, but other meats like salami, tinned ham and sausages have fat added to them in production

- high-fat dairy foods – cheeses, particularly hard cheeses, whole milk, creamy and Greek yoghurts
- butter and margarine
- cakes and biscuits
- fried food
- mayonnaise and salad dressings

Reading food labels will also help you to really understand the amount of fat in various manufactured foods. More on this later in this chapter.

Portion sizes

As already noted, the portion sizes of many snacks and manufactured foods have increased substantially over recent years. This is likely to have had a substantial effect on people's struggles to control weight.

Larger portion sizes are now common in a whole range of different snack foods, manufactured products and meals served in restaurants, to the point where large portions are becoming the norm. Most people will finish whatever is placed in front of them, regardless of whether they were served a large, average or small portion. Although larger portions are perceived as better value, it is important to be aware of how they can interfere with your plans to manage weight. Look out for "big eats", "king size", "X% extra free", "buy one get one free" offers or "eat as much as you can". Although these seem to offer value for money, they won't be beneficial to your health unless the offer relates to fruit, vegetables or wholegrain cereals – and it invariably doesn't.

If you want more guidance on portion sizes, check out www.bdaweightwise.com.

Soft drinks and alcohol

Alcohol is a high-calorie drink which if taken in large amounts can prevent weight loss. For health reasons it is suggested that men drink no more than 21 units of alcohol a week (no more than 4 units per day) and women no more than 14 units per week (no more than 3 units per day). A unit of alcohol is a small glass of wine, half a pint of beer or lager or one pub measure of spirits or sherry. Keeping within these health limits is often sufficient for people to also lose weight, although for some people it may be necessary to restrict alcohol a little further. Apart from the calories in alcohol itself, drinking it tends to make people feel hungrier, leading to difficulties in coping with planned food changes.

Of course alcohol can be included as part of a healthy diet. There is no need to stop it completely unless you've been advised to do so by your doctor for other reasons.

Keeping a record of eating habits will help to highlight how much or how often you drink alcohol and what effect, if any, this has on your eating habits. If you feel that your drinking is a little high or it leads to eating more than planned, it might be an idea to think through ways of limiting alcohol. The choice of how you achieve this is yours. If you drink at home rather than socially, you might limit the amount of alcohol around at home or you might measure spirits using a 25ml spirit measure that is equivalent to one unit. Alternatively, it may be that drinking socially is a regular feature of your lifestyle. If this is the case you might for example change from pints to half pints or alternate between diet soft drinks and alcohol or try diluting alcohol with sugar free mixers to make drinks last longer.

Soft drinks and mixers can be full of sugar, with an average can containing about ten teaspoons. If drunk in large amounts, sweetened drinks can interfere with weight loss. Recent research in children suggests that such drinks may play a very important role in weight gain. It is thought that our bodies don't recognize the sugar and calories from drinks in the way that it would from food. Also, the portion size of soft drinks in many restaurants and supermarket has increased substantially over recent years. So if sweetened soft drinks are a regular feature in your diet it may be worth considering making a change. Diet drinks and sugar-free squashes are better alternatives to sugary soft drinks. The healthiest drink of all though is water – either still or sparkling.

Understanding Food Labels

It can be terribly confusing to look at nutrition labels, but learning to understand them can be very helpful in making truly informed choices about which products to buy. It is certainly better than trusting the manufacturer's promises on the front of the package. Manufacturers are given guidelines about using nutritional claims on the front of their products, but it is always wise to turn the product over and check what it really contains.

These are the guidelines given for fat-related claims:

- Low-fat products should contain less than 3g of fat per 100g.
- Fat-free products should contain less than 0.15g fat per 100g.
- Reduced-fat products should contain less than ¾ of the fat in original product.

Take a look at the nutrition labels below from a reduced-fat packet of digestive biscuits and a standard pack of digestives.

At first sight they may look terribly confusing. In fact, for managing weight only some parts are important. The key is to keep things simple and to look initially only at total fat (sometimes just referred to as "fat") and calories. Calories on nutritional labels are referred to as "kilocalories", "kcal" for short.

Nutrition

Average Values	Per Biscuit	Per 100g
Energy	292kJ	1983kJ
	70kcal	473kcal
Protein	1.1g	7.2g
Carbohydrate	9.2g	62.6g
of which sugars	2.4g	16.6g
Fat	3.2g	21.5g
of which saturates	1.5g	10.1g
Fibre	0.5g	3.6g
Sodium	0.1g	0.6g
per biscuit	70 calories	3.2g fat

Nutrition

Average Values	Per Biscuit	Per 100g
Energy	275 kJ	1870 kJ
	65 kcal	445 kcal
Protein	1.1 g	7.2 g
Carbohydrate	10.0 g	67.7 g
of which sugars	3.0 g	20.3 g
Fat	2.4 g	16.1 g
of which saturates	1.1 g	7.5 g
Fibre	0.5 g	3.5 g
Sodium	0.1 g	0.6 g
Per Biscuit	65 calories	2.4g fat

Standard digestive biscuit   Reduced fat digestive biscuit

As a general guide, low-fat food contains less than 3g fat per 100g and high-fat food contains 20g per 100g. The aim is to compare products and choose the option with the lowest fat and calorie content.

The easiest way to compare these two labels is to look at the "per 100g" column. Compare the "total fat" and the "calories" per 100g. The reduced fat version has 16.1g of fat, 445 kcal, and the standard 21.5g fat and 473 kcal. This means that choosing one reduced-fat digestive (about 14g each) will only save 2g fat and 5 kcal compared to the standard biscuit – hardly the calorie-free option they are sometimes perceived to be. This is very common in many reduced-fat sweet foods such as cakes and biscuits where the fat content has been reduced but extra sugars or other carbohydrates have been added to ensure the taste of the lower-fat product remains comparable. So the bottom line is that you may be eating a lower-fat biscuit but its calorie count is very similar to the original so it isn't really going to be helpful in managing weight.

However, there are some lower-fat foods where the differences compared to the original are greater than the above example and such foods can be more helpful in limiting fat and calorie intake. Examples of some of these foods include lower-fat spreads, fat-free salad dressings and low-fat milk. The choice of whether to use any of these products depends on whether you feel this would limit your enjoyment of various foods and if such changes seem sustainable. If you love a particular high-fat food and can't bear the thought of changing to a lower-fat version, then consider other ways of limiting fat intake.

There is no one dietary approach for managing weight that suits everybody, with different treatments being helpful to some and not to others. Experimenting to find the approach that works for you and how to overcome the challenges that will arise in keeping food (and activity) changes in place is an essential part of this process. However it is important to choose dietary changes that will not only help you to lose and maintain weight but will also promote foods known to be protective for health – principally more fruit, vegetables and wholegrain cereals. A summary of the key points to consider in making successful long term changes to eating is presented below.

Summary

- Use food and activity monitoring to increase awareness of eating and identify the triggers to eating more than planned (*see Chapter 3*).
- Establish a regular eating pattern. Skipping meals often leads to difficulties with portion control or food choices later in the day. There are no rigid rules about what time to eat, but many people find their bodies need food every three to four hours.
- Thinking through previous attempts at changing eating habits can be helpful in working out what was helpful and what was not.
- Food changes need to be realistic and sustainable.
- Small changes added together make a big difference to weight control over time.
- Allow time for changes to eating and activity behaviour to occur. Changing any type of behaviour is complicated and requires a fair bit of experimenting.
- Avoid striving for perfection. It isn't necessary to follow the "perfect" diet in order to lose weight. Instead, try to find a better way of eating that you are happy to continue with long term.
- Planning ahead helps ensure healthy foods and meals are available. This avoids the need to buy food on impulse or grab whatever might be available at the last minute.
- Whatever method you choose, more fruit and vegetables, more wholegrains and fewer fatty foods is the basis for all healthy approaches to managing weight.
- Portion sizes are a very important aspect of eating more healthily. Over recent years standard portion sizes have become larger, providing extra calories without people really realizing this is happening.

6

Making the Changes in Daily Life

"I thought that this book was about changing habits. But I've got halfway through and I haven't actually done anything yet! I want to get on with it!"

"There are a lot more things that I need to sort out before I can begin to change. It's all very well talking about changing eating and activity, but I have lots of emotional issues that need to be fixed first."

Some people, quite rightly, want to get on with things at this point. It is now time to do so. This chapter covers the process of beginning to change your life.

This may seem a little too soon to some – what if there are issues to deal with concerning emotions and other people (*Chapters 7 and 8*)? However, there are only so many things that can be worked out in advance. There comes a time when it is better to get started and then deal with the remaining issues when they come up. Now is the time to begin the tricky but exciting process of trying out new things in your life.

Making Plans That Will Work

The key to weight loss is finding plans that work for you. Not all plans will work. This is not a problem! In this chapter you will develop your abilities at being creative, making good plans and solving problems. You will start to work out what works for you.

Of course there are plans that clearly will not work. It is worth being able to spot these, so that you can save time and avoid getting discouraged. For example, saying "I plan to cut down on the calories a bit" is so vague that it is probably useless. How would you know if you were succeeding or not? How much, exactly, is "a bit"? Equally, plans can be very clear but unlikely to work. If you planned to spend two hours in the gym every night of the week (and decided that your family would just have to put up with it), you would be unlikely to keep it up for very long.

To succeed you need a plan that is sensible, clear, realistic and designed to fit into your life. Happily, everybody can come up with plans like this, as long as they follow a few simple rules.

Weaving the changes into your daily life

If a person wants to lose a significant amount of weight for the long term, they will have to make clear changes in their lives. However, this does not mean that they have to turn their life inside out. We know very well that big plans often fail quite quickly. There is a smarter way to change habits: make changes that fit into daily life and schedule. Instead of breaking up their usual routine, a person can look hard at their routine and work out how to make changes that fit into it – or even take advantage of it. Habits can become part of a regular and simple routine. Most people brush their teeth, for example, as part of their morning schedule. There are a few important points to think about here:

1. Most people do not think that brushing their teeth is a huge effort.
2. Most people do it automatically, without thinking about it.
3. People do not often forget to brush their teeth, even if their routine changes (for example, if they are on holiday) because it is a really strong habit and it is part of their personal morning or evening routine.

4. When we were children, it may have seemed like a real hassle to brush our teeth. However, when it became a habit, it became no problem at all.

It would be great if eating and exercise habits could be like this! Of course, eating and exercise are a bit more complicated than tooth-brushing, but they can also fit easily and flexibly into a person's life.

Many people find it hard to include a period of exercise in their day for example, yet, as we have seen, it may only take a small adjustment to make significant changes. For example, a person could walk more on their way to and from work, perhaps getting off of the bus or parking their car a mile further away. Most of us have plenty of times in our week when we could walk rather than drive or be a passenger. This is a good example of smart change from the inside out.

The principle also applies to some issues around eating. For example, if a person decides that lunch with their friends is a time when they are likely to eat too much, they can either cancel the lunches or try to arrange a change of venue to a place where there are many more healthy options on offer. One solution would break up their routine, whereas the other would work with that routine. This is the approach that is helpful: to try to "go with the grain" and where possible fit a plan into the natural course of your life.

"But I don't have a routine!"

However, some people may not be able to benefit from these ideas as much as they would like, as they do not have much of a daily routine.

This is a tricky situation, as a person is unlikely to succeed in weight loss if they do not have any routine at all. Eating needs to happen fairly regularly – if there are long gaps between meals, a person will get hungry and binge. Equally, if a person just "grazes" and snacks the whole time without any meals they will probably gain weight fast. Activity also has to happen regularly if it is going to work – not just occasionally, or lots in one week and none in the next. So if you do not have a routine, it is important to get one. You can use all of the planning tools below to get you started.

SMART Planning

Sometimes, planning is fairly easy. However, when it comes to changing habits a little more effort is required. Very often, habits around eating and exercise are very "stuck" and difficult to change. Also, it can be hard to know whether you have made any effective changes or not. This is why the SMART method of planning can be useful. SMART is a way to remember what makes a good plan. It stands for:

S   Simple (and specific)
M   Measurable
A   Agreed (and achievable)
R   Realistic
T   on a Timescale

If a plan is all of these, it has the best chance of success. Here is an explanation of each category.

Simple (and specific)

This means that a plan is very clear and precise, but not complicated. Vague plans generally do not work. For example "I will cut down on chocolate a bit" is quite vague and it would be hard to know whether you were succeeding. However, "I will have no more than three chocolate bars in a week" is a specific plan. It is also simple, which is essential. If you are going to be able to stick to it in the middle of a busy life, it is best if it isn't complicated.

There is a good way to test this – imagine that you are explaining your plan to a ten-year-old child. If the child understands it, and could even do it if asked, then it is simple enough.

If not, then work on it. Write it down in really simple words and throw out any part that you do not really need.

Measurable

Remember Amounts Count? If a person is going to do some exercise or make a change to their eating patterns, it is critical to be able to answer questions like "How much?" or "How often?" Someone might decide that they want to "walk a lot more", but if they do not make clear how much more they are planning to do, they will probably end up doing a lot one week and much less the following week. Make sure you are clear about amounts in your planning.

Agreed (and achievable)

This reminds you to check that you have enough support to do your plan. Are your surroundings set up so that they will support your plan? Do you have the support of the people who might affect your plan? Can you do something about this? (More on this in the next chapter.)

Realistic

This is one of the most important parts of a good plan. It must be realistic. This means being sure that it is not too difficult or too ambitious. It is better to start small than to go for a huge project. You can then achieve your goals and move on to more ambitious things. However, if you plan big things and then fail, you have lost time that you could have spent on a good plan and probably become discouraged into the bargain.

on a Timescale

There are two parts to this. First, when will your plan start? Second, when will you check if it is working? Good planners always decide on exact dates for both of these events. Checking is essential – if you find you are achieving your plan easily, then you might decide to move on to something more challenging. On the other hand, if it is not going at all well then you need to try to work out what is going wrong. Checking makes sure that you will not struggle on with a bad plan forever.

When you are thinking about when to check your plan, remember that new habits can take some time to get used to, so it is a bad idea to check too soon.

Write down when you are going to review your plan in your diary or on your calendar. If you don't have any kind of diary or calendar, get one.

Some examples

Hopefully, you now have some idea of how to make SMART plans. However, it is very useful to see some SMART planning in action. Here are some ideas that weren't very SMART, but became SMART with a bit of thought:

A not-very-SMART plan
"I'm just going to eat less. Of everything."

A SMART plan
"Starting next week, I am going to cut down on portion sizes for my main meals. I will choose slightly smaller plates to put my food on and I won't just pile the food up twice as high! I will probably have to make sure that I eat bulky food like pasta to fill me up. I'll carry on having biscuits with my coffee at work, but I will make sure I don't have more than three a day. Nothing else changes – I'm going to keep it simple and try not to break up my routine too much. I'll do this for four weeks and see how I am doing."

Another not-very-SMART plan
"Walking is good, and I don't mind doing it. I'm definitely going to walk more and see how it goes."

A SMART plan

"Walking is good, and I don't mind doing it. Starting next week, I am going to get off one bus stop earlier on my way to and back from work and walk the rest of the way. I'm also going to make sure that I get one long walk in at the weekend. I don't mind when it is – I'm going to keep that flexible – but it will definitely happen and it will last for at least 45 minutes. I'll try this for three weeks and see how it is going. I'll be interested to see whether I am a bit fitter –and enjoying it – or whether I need a bit more variety in my activity routine."

Some people may think that all of this hard-edged planning is a good idea for businesses, but not for people, or may believe that people change in a "deep" or "spiritual" way, not by step-by-step planning. We can only respond that our clinical experience shows that SMART works. Try it. If you are reading this book, it is probably because many of your previous strategies have not worked in the long term. Try this one instead.

Temptations and Bad Ideas

There is one final point about planning, and it is possibly the most important point of all: should you be trying out completely new plans for behaviour change or sticking to methods that you know work?

It is only natural to look at what has worked before. However, it is important to be very careful when thinking about this.

Pete likes the ideas in this book but in the past he has some short-term success with extreme weight-loss methods:

"Weight loss is incredibly difficult for me – but I do know something that works. I can lose two stone fairly fast if I follow this particular diet. It is pretty simple and easy to stick to. Thanks to reading this book, this time I'm going to focus on exercise as well. And I can use all of the stuff about thoughts and motivation to

> *keep going. If I keep to these fairly simple (and very small) meals and steer clear of chocolate, I can keep it up. Unfortunately, the moment I go off track – or eat even a bit of chocolate – then I tend to be in trouble. So I'll stick to my routine. I've got to do what works best for me."*

Clearly, Pete is trying to use what he has learned in the past. However, it is interesting that he thinks that his favourite diet "works". If you asked him why, he would tell you that he lost weight three times by using it. Unfortunately, each time he put it all back on. If he thought hard about it, Pete would realize that his diet does not work – it has failed, again and again, to give him weight loss for the long term.

It is important for you to have faith in your own judgement about the way you lose weight. However, it is always a good idea to be cautious about extreme weight loss methods. They may look good and promise fast results, but so do a lot of other plans that don't work in the long term.

Don't Wait – Start Planning Now

You may have some good plans in your head for weight loss already. However, you might need a bit more time to get ready. It is important to have faith in your own ability to plan. Remember that no one knows your life better than you do. However, if you are really stuck for ideas, don't worry. There are some good tips further on in this chapter.

If you have any ideas, or beginnings of ideas, start to make them clear. It is important to write everything down. Even if your ideas are not very clear right now, try to get:

- Two plans for activity/exercise
- Two plans for eating

You can write your plans on the planning form on page 138. This form makes you think in a SMART way and gets your ideas down on paper. There is another blank copy of this form in Appendix I, so that you can use these forms as often as you need to.

Once you've written them down, you do not need to start all four plans at once. It is up to you to decide which to start with and how many to try at any one time. However, there are a few good ideas to follow in deciding what to start with:

1. Pick plans that you have a good chance of succeeding with. You can always add more changes later if you find it all too easy.
2. Make sure you have a mixture of activity/exercise plans and plans about food. The smart move is to do both. This is what the "experts" – the NWCR group – did.
3. Don't wait. There are always lots of (bad) reasons to start "some other time". If your own reasons (from Chapter 1) tell you that losing weight is worth doing, then it is worth starting right now.

What to do if you are dreading getting started with your plans

If the thought of starting your plans is really frightening or you find that you are making lots of excuses to get started, check through the following:

Thoughts
Catch your thoughts and keep catching them. Keep a particular lookout for thoughts like "This will never work" or "This will be awful", "I've got to do it perfectly all the time" or "It's too much effort". Question and expand these.

Motivation and reasons
Do you have good reasons to do your plan? Even more importantly, do you have your reasons in your mind whilst you are starting? If you can't remember why you are making all this effort, you will probably never get started.

Activity/exercise plans

- What exactly is the plan? (Amounts Count!)

- What help do you need for your plan?
  Whose support would be helpful?

- When are you going to start, and when are
  you going to check and review your plan?

Eating/food plans

- What exactly is the plan? (Amounts Count!)

- What help do you need for your plan?
  Whose support would be helpful?

- When are you going to start, and when are
  you going to check and review your plan?

Reasons

- What are the good reasons for spending time
  and effort making these plans work?

The way you are doing it

One reason why you might be dreading getting started is that
your plan is too extreme. It might just be too hard, or too boring,
or never leave room for treats. Remember, your plan should be
something that you could imagine doing for the rest of your life.

Doing It – Putting the Plan into Practice

"This has given me a lot to think about. I need to practise my planning skills. It is really important for me to get my plans right before I start – I don't want to do something that is too difficult, or not clear enough. I will keep working on my planning skills."

"This has given me some good ideas. The SMART ideas have allowed me to make my plan better. It's not perfect, but it is time to get on and do it anyway. There will probably be problems, but I can't tell what they will be until I try."

Which one of these two people will succeed in making serious changes to their habits over the next six months?

Once you have one or two plans that you are happy to start with, it is best to just get on with them. No one can really say how a plan will work out before it is actually tried. So it is best to get on and try it. It may be much easier than you expected!

Whilst carrying out your plan, here are some good ideas to bear in mind:

- Remember your reasons. These will give you strength to keep going.
- Keep noticing your thinking patterns. Biased and unhelpful thoughts may cause you problems – spot them and then use your skills from Chapter 2 to resolve them.
- Write down things that might be useful for the future – either helpful things or blocks. It will help when you review your plan.
- Don't change your plan as you go along. Keep going and try to make it work. Of course, if you break your leg you may have to change your exercise plan. Otherwise, keep going, even if it's going badly, and try to write down what the problems are.
- Notice how things change over time. Are the changes getting easier? Is anything about your appetite or fitness changing?

These are pretty much the only things to keep in mind whilst doing a plan. Otherwise, just do it!

Checking – How Did It All Go?

After a while, it will be time to check your plan. Did it go well? What could be done better? How could you solve the problems you came across?

Kirsty is checking over her two plans and is having some very useful thoughts about them:

"Today is the day – it has been four weeks. I think that things have gone pretty well. I had two main plans – first, to walk further on the way to and from work, and also to have a long walk at the weekend. Second, I was going to cut down slightly on portion sizes for main meals – and put a limit on biscuits!

"I think that I have done well. I have stuck to both plans about 90 per cent. It has not been perfect – bad weather stopped me from walking once or twice, and I'm really bad at controlling my portions when I'm out with friends. Anyway, apart from that it was a success and I should be proud of myself. I'm planning to take myself shopping to celebrate this weekend.

"I think that it worked well to have realistic plans that didn't take up too much of my time or mess up my life too much.

"There are two main things that I need to do differently. First of all, I need to work out what to do about bad weather when I am walking. To be honest, this is not really that difficult. When I look at my reasons, they are really important – I'm not going to let a bit of rain come between me and my goals. I'll just get the right clothes and get on with it. However, the problem with eating sensible amounts when I am with friends is a difficult one. I'm not sure what to do about this and I need to give it some more thought."

As well as having a really honest look at how well her plans went, Kirsty is thinking about what she can learn from the whole process. You can do it too by following the steps below.

Did you stick to your plan?

Ask yourself honestly how well your plan went. It should have been Measurable, so it should be easy to see how successful you were. At this point the only question is whether you managed to actually do the plan – that is, whether you managed to change your behaviour. There are two things that it's *not* about right now:

It's not about whether you lost weight
At this point, only think about the behaviour, not about the weight. Whether you actually carried out your plan is far more important. Changing your behaviour is what is needed to control your weight in the long term, so focus on that.

Remember that there may be quite a few steps to go through before you really start losing weight. Your goals might be quite small at the moment, but you can build up to bigger things later.

It's not about whether you had fun doing the plan
You are doing this so that you can lose weight, and you are losing weight because this is really important to you. It might be enjoyable, it might be difficult – the main point is whether you managed to do it at all.

Obviously, it does matter if you struggled through your plan and it was absolutely awful and didn't get any better with time. This is unlikely to be a good plan for the long term. Otherwise, weight loss is about doing things that really matter, for seriously important personal reasons. The reasons are exactly the same whether the process is easy and enjoyable or difficult. Imagine a person who said, "I'd love to have children – but only so long as it was enjoyable." Or another person who said, "I am going to register for a degree course at university – but I will only keep doing it so long as it is enjoyable." With any important task that involves serious changes to your life, there will be good times and bad times. It is important not to get discouraged about your weight-loss plans when you are having a bad time. It could all look completely different next week.

Recognize your achievement!

If you managed to succeed with a plan, then you have done something that is worth celebrating! It doesn't matter whether it was a big plan or a small plan. If you made a good plan and then followed it, you have done well. Long-term habits of eating and activity are hard to change, so recognize your achievement by rewarding yourself. Take yourself shopping or to see a movie – it does not have to be huge reward, but give yourself a treat. However, it is probably not wise to get into the habit of rewarding yourself with food!

If you are uncomfortable with the idea of rewarding yourself, try to spot the thoughts that come up when you think about it. It may be worth questioning and expanding these. In the mean-time, give yourself a pat on the back. You have done something that you didn't have to do and that will move you towards your important reasons for change.

Think about what you can learn

Very often, plans do not go quite as you expect. Sometimes they go wrong; sometimes they turn out better than expected. Either way, there are useful lessons to be learned.

There is a simple but useful way to learn from your experiences:

- Think about your plan and look at any notes that you made whilst you were doing it.
- Then think about two things: what Worked Well (the WWs) and what you would Do Differently (the DDs).

The WWs are really useful. It is always a good idea to look at success – and there may be a way to weave these WWs into your next plan. On the other hand, the DDs need some more thought. You might have some ideas about what you could Do Differently, or you might be really stuck. Sometimes something just went badly and it is not easy to see how it could be fixed.

Don't give up on these issues – we will look at them more closely later.

Decide what you are going to do next

Once you have tried your plan and analysed how it worked, you can think about what you are going to do next. This is really up to you. If you found your plan difficult, you might just want to do it again for a while. You will probably have some good ideas about how to do it a little better a second time round. Remember that the aim here is to get new habits that will last for the long term, so it is not a bad idea to keep doing the same thing until it is really easy and natural. On the other hand, it is important to move along and develop. Amounts Count – if you are going to lose a serious amount of weight, then your habits may have to change quite a bit, and this will be a long road. Use your judgement, and remember that if things don't go well it is not a disaster, but something to learn from.

However, if something is really stopping you from carrying out your plans, it is time to use some serious problem-solving skills.

Problem-Solving: The Master Class

Very often, you will be able to look at a problem and easily think of a solution. However, sometimes it will be more difficult. If you are going to become an expert at weight loss, you will need to develop your skills at solving difficult problems. The good news is that you do not need to be a genius to solve problems and you do not have to wait for "inspiration" or "a brilliant idea" to come into your head. There are smart, simple ways of thinking about problems give a great chance of thinking up smart, simple solutions.

Of course, problem-solving is not just about fixing things that have gone badly wrong. It is more about being flexible and creative. Flexibility really matters. No one will ever find a plan that will work perfectly for them for the rest of their lives. Different situations will mean different plans – but that will keep the process of weight loss from getting boring!

Research shows that regular problem-solving keeps weight off

It seems obvious that people who are flexible and can solve problems will do better at weight loss. However, there is also hard research evidence that shows this. The evidence also shows that problem-solving is particularly important for keeping weight off in the long term.

The study, published in 2001, started with a group of overweight people who all managed to lose some weight using CBT. However, at the end of the CBT course, different people got different treatment. Some carried on meeting regularly in "problem-solving groups" that used clear techniques to solve their weight-loss difficulties. Others got no follow up. After 18 months *five times as many* of the problem-solving group had managed to keep a good amount of weight off (more than 10 per cent) compared to the group without follow up.

This is great research, but most people do not have a local weight-loss problem-solving group. However, although it might be impossible to do exactly what the research group did, there is one thing that anyone can do: learn the problem-solving techniques used by the successful group and use them regularly.

Techniques for problem-solving

Trying to find a way to solve a problem is like trying to find buried treasure in a field. Imagine that you do not know exactly where the treasure is, but you are pretty sure it is there. How would you go about finding it?

1. You need to look. The treasure – or the solution to your problem – cannot be seen straight away. It will not come to you – you have to go and find it.

2. You need to be systematic. If you just started digging randomly in the field, you would not get very far. You need a clear step-by-step plan of action.
3. Don't stop too soon. With buried treasure, you might be digging just a couple of yards away from it, but you would not know that you had been close until you finally found it. It is the same with solutions to really difficult problems. You might not think that a solution is possible – that is, until the moment when you see the answer.

With good techniques, you can make sure that your search for solutions is really effective. Good problem-solving technique only takes a few steps – five, in fact.

The five steps of problem-solving

The whole process of problem-solving is easy to understand. Here are the five steps:

1. Define your problem.
2. Make up lots of alternative solutions.
3. Analyse your alternatives.
4. Try out your solution(s).
5. See how it went – and do it again!

Let's take them one at a time.

Define your problem

In order to solve your problem, you need to be very clear about what the problem actually is. First, it needs to be something that can be solved – something fairly clear and of a fairly manageable size. "Achieving world peace" might be a great goal, but it is not a sensible target for problem-solving. The problem should also not be too fuzzy – for example, "I want to be happier." If you find that your problem is really big or really fuzzy, try to break it down into smaller parts.

When you have your clearly defined problem, then ask yourself, "Is this *really* the problem?" This may sound odd. However, let's look at it in practice. Here is **Kirsty's** problem:

"I really don't know what to do about eating when I am out with friends. I always try to stick to my plan – which is to eat smaller portions. But it never happens! I see my friends quite a lot, so eating big meals when I am out with them is really beginning to add up. I don't want to stop seeing my friends. But I don't know what to do about the portions. I know what I want to do, but it just isn't happening."

Is this really Kirsty's problem? Or:

- Is it really the size of her meals or is it the type of food – if she had a huge salad, would it matter?
- Is it really the meals that she has with her friends? If she ate less for the rest of the day before she saw her friends, would a big meal in the evening matter?
- If she did a lot of exercise on that day, would the big meal matter?

You can see that if a problem is approached from a few different angles, it may look completely different.

Make up lots of alternative solutions

Even when you have stated your problem clearly, it is hard to just "be creative" about solutions. However, there are techniques that give us the best chance of coming up with new ideas.

One of the most important techniques is in two different stages. The first stage is where you make up alternatives. In this stage, you are just thinking up ideas. You should not be thinking about whether they will work or whether they are sensible – that comes in the next stage. For now, you just need ideas – and lots of them.

Get a piece of paper and start writing down ideas. Anything goes. No idea is too silly or too unrealistic. If you are stuck, then it is a good idea to start off with some really silly ideas. Choose something really stupid and funny. For some reason, this seems to help to "unblock" our thinking and get us moving. When you are moving, just keep going until you have *at least five new ideas* – but it would be even better if you could get 10 or 15.

We can follow Kirsty through this process:

- "Ugh, I'm really stuck with this one. OK, I will start with something silly to get myself going: I could hire a private detective to follow me and stop me if I ordered something too big!"
- "Wouldn't it be great if there were restaurants that only served small portions . . ."
- "I could decide in advance what I was going to eat – we usually go to the same places. That way I could avoid having to make a decision 'on the spot'."
- "I could eat less, or exercise more, on the day I'm going to go out. I could see it as 'paying' for my evening meal – I 'pay' for the meal with a good long gym session."
- "I could get my friends to check whether I am eating a sensible-sized meal."
- "I could get the big meal and then leave some."
- "I could choose a smaller meal and promise myself I could have more if I felt like it."
- "I could choose a big portion of something without much energy in it – maybe salad or vegetables."
- "I could have a filling snack before I go out, so that I feel less like eating lots."
- "How about a reward – if I manage to choose sensible portions for a whole month, I will take myself shopping."
- "Or maybe a punishment – if I don't do it I will give a donation to a political party that I really hate!"

That is a pretty good session. There are 11 separate ideas there. Some are silly – like the private detective! – and others are not very smart, like trying to motivate yourself through punishment. But this does not matter. At this stage, anything goes. The process of analysing ideas comes next.

Analyse your alternatives
Now you have your list of ideas, it is time to make some decisions about them. There are three steps here:

1. Throw out the options that really will not work.
2. Work out how good the other options would be in the short, medium and long term.
3. Always remember that you are trying to build positive habits that will stay with you.

First, you can throw out the obviously unworkable ideas. However, you must be careful. Some ideas might seem silly but contain something positive. For example, Kirsty thought the "small-portions restaurant" was a silly idea, but there is some truth to it.

Second, look at the other options and work out how they would actually fit into your life. Remember to think about the long term as well as the short term. Kirsty's idea of having a snack before going out seems reasonable, but how would it work in the long term? Is this a habit she wants to build into her life? There are no simple answers to this question, but it is important to think hard about your own life and habits to see what is likely to work. Remember, you are trying to build positive new habits.

Kirsty's decision-making went like this:

> *"Well, I can throw out a few ideas straight away. The private detective, obviously! Also, I really don't think that I can rely on my friends to help me out with portion size. Most of them have their own issues with weight – I'm not sure they could help. Also, I can't really imagine getting into the habit of leaving food on my plate. Maybe it would be a good habit, but I love food and I believe in eating what I have paid for! Also, the 'filling snack' before I go*

*out sounds good, but knowing me and my habits, that could turn
into a very bad habit fast.*

"The 'punishment' idea would work for a while, but it is not a
habit that I want to build into my life. I think that there are three
things I could do that would work and would become good habits.
I'm going to try:"

Getting some exercise on days when I know I'm going out
in the evening

Deciding in advance what I am going to eat, and

For the next couple of months, rewarding myself if I get
it right.

"I like these options – it seems like a good habit to get more
exercise and remember that food is not a 'problem' – it's the
balance of food and activity that matters. Also, I like the habit of
deciding in advance – it means that nothing really changes about
my routine with my friends, I just get a little more planning and
control into my food choices. Finally, rewarding myself keeps
everything positive."

Kirsty has done some great problem-solving. Her ideas are
sensible and would work in the long term. Of course, this does
not mean that they are guaranteed to work. Ideas have to be
tested in real life.

Try out your solution
This is the fun part. Now you get to try out a new way of doing
things. The results will not always be perfect, but they will usually
be different, and in a stuck situation anything new can be useful.

When you try out your new solution(s), try to make it as
SMART as possible. Keep it simple and clear. Also, give it some
time to work. Not all solutions – even good ones – will work
overnight. However, make sure that you do get on and try it.
Without actually testing it out, you will never know if it works.

See how it went – and do it again!
So, did it work? Could you actually make your solution happen?
A perfect solution is not much help if you cannot actually put

it into practice. Secondly, did it fix your problem? If so, how well did it work? Is the problem completely solved? Or did the solution make absolutely no difference? Of course, these are not the only options. Very often, an idea will work a little bit, but not as well as you hoped.

If the solution *was* perfect then the problem-solving process is over for now, because the problem is solved. However, if things went badly – or just not very well – you can start the whole process again.

Don't give up if it did not work. Imagine if any of the great scientists had given up when they had failed to solve a problem the first time. What would you think of a police detective who had just one idea to solve a murder case and then gave up when it was clear that this idea was wrong? Remember that a solution may be very close, but you just can't see it. Also, even if you got a solution that was alright but not great, there may be an even better one close by.

But What about Weight Loss?

"Hold on – isn't something missing? I thought this was all about losing weight!"

This whole book is about losing weight. Yet we have been focusing on plans and changes in behaviour – why?

In most dieting approaches, checking weight regularly is extremely important. It is the way to check whether you are succeeding. This is not a bad idea. It is forces you to be honest – it is hard to cheat the scales. However, focusing on weight leads to problems:

1. It makes people choose fast weight-loss methods.
2. If they are losing weight, they think their diet is "working".
3. If they are not losing weight, they think they have "failed".

All of these can be a problem. Losing weight, however, quickly, does not mean that a diet is "working" for the long term. Also, if a person thinks that they have "failed" when they do not lose weight, it is easy to imagine all of the destructive thoughts that go with this.

That's why book focuses not on weight but on changing eating and activity habits. These are what must change if weight is going to stay off in the long term. If you take in less energy in food and burn off more in exercise, then weight loss *will* follow.

However, what if you are trying out your plans and weight loss is not happening? If you think that you have changed your eating and activity a lot, but are not losing weight, you will need to think about what you are doing.

In general, if plans are happening but weight is not changing, three things can be occurring:

1. You are not clear about what is actually needed for weight loss. For example, if you a) eat fewer biscuits in a week, b) go for a gentle 15-minute swim twice per week and c) expect to lose lots of weight, then you will be disappointed. This may well be a good start, but Amounts Count. More than this will be needed.

2. You are not sticking to your plans as well as you think you are. Remember, we are is not very good at remembering details. You may be eating more and exercising less than you think.

3. You do not understand something important about food or activity. For example, people have been encouraged to use lots of olive oil because it is healthy. Of course, compared to some other oils, it is healthier. However, it is still pure fat, and if you use lots of it, you will gain weight. Misunderstandings like this are very common, even in people who see themselves as "experts" at dieting. Bear in mind that there are errors and mistakes in everybody's knowledge, including your own.

If your plans seem to be sensible but are not producing weight loss, then there are a couple of simple steps to take. First, it is useful to start recording activity and eating again. This will make it clear if your plans are being followed and if there are any confusions about amounts of food or exercise. Second, it is a good idea to get some help from a registered dietician. The problem with misunderstandings about food is that we do not realize that we are misunderstanding.

Weight loss will only happen if you change your habits. Thinking about change or trying to find out the "reasons" for being overweight are fine – but they do not change anything on their own. Also, no one will succeed by just one change – this is a process of trying out new things, keeping what works and changing what does not work. Problems will come up that need to be solved. Unhelpful thoughts will certainly be around, and it is a good idea to have your reasons for change clearly in your mind. However, this is generally a fun process. It is about doing something new in a flexible way and making plans that are designed to fit well into your life. Not everything will work straight away, but that is probably not a surprise! The important thing is to try something new and to be honest about what works. With each new plan, you will become more of an expert on your own weight loss.

Summary

- Get started – some times it is best to just get going.
- Make SMART plans that fit into your life.
- Watch out for extreme dieting habits.
- Carry out your plan and check whether it works.
- Actively try to solve any problems that come up.

7

Hunger, Fullness and Being Upset

> "I have some great plans, but it doesn't take a genius to see why they don't work out. Whenever I'm bored or stressed, I just stuff myself. My plans go out of the window."
>
> "I have no idea what is going wrong. As far as I can tell, I shouldn't even need to have weight-loss plans! I eat when I am hungry and I don't eat when I don't feel like it. But I still put on weight."

You may have SMART and sensible plans about eating and exercise. However, what happens if your plans are knocked off course by strong emotions or cravings? This chapter shows you how to spot the emotions or sensations that are getting in your way – and what to do about them.

Most people understand "comfort eating", or "emotional eating". Most of us have at some time felt very low, or very bored, and eaten a lot because of this. Sometimes, emotional eating seems to be an overweight person's biggest problem – there are people who seem to be sad or angry a lot of the time, and they can't stop eating when they feel like this. Other people know that they cannot control their cravings – once cravings for a particular type of food start, eating that food seems to be the only way to stop them.

It may seem that emotional eating and food cravings are easy to understand – bad feelings and strong cravings can make us eat more. However, things are very often more complicated than this. Have a look at the statements below. All of them involve some kind of feeling which is affecting the person's weight-loss plans:

- "I'm exhausted. I'm too tired to go for a walk."
- "This is a great meal! I can't wait for dessert. Bring it on!"
- "I need to have some more to eat. I don't feel full yet."
- "I'm in such a good mood. Life is too short to spend it exercising!"
- "I look so fat, I can't eat anything else today."
- "I can't stop craving chocolate. I must make sure that there is never any of it in – or even near! – the house."

You may recognize some of these situations – they are common in people trying to lose weight. However, it is clear that the feelings in these situations – and their effects – go beyond simple "comfort eating". There are a couple of useful things to notice:

1. Feelings can certainly affect eating. However, they affect *activity and exercise too*.
2. It's not just bad feelings that are important. *Good* feelings, like enjoyment and relaxation, can also make a person eat more or be less active.

All of these situations have one thing in common – the feelings are in charge, not the weight-loss plan. This cannot be allowed to happen if you are serious about losing weight.

Different Emotions and Sensations

Which feelings are important for your personal weight-loss plan? Lots of different feeling can affect weight loss, so it is a good idea to start out by thinking about as many as possible. The table below shows 20 different types and gives an idea of the range we are talking about. It splits "feelings" into two different categories: emotions, like anger, fear or sadness, and also physical sensations, like tiredness, hunger and cravings. Both can be important for weight loss.

Emotions	Sensations
Sadness	Hunger
Fear or anxiety	Tiredness
Boredom	An empty stomach
Anger or frustration	Cravings
Happiness	Feeling sick or dizzy
Resentment	Pain or soreness
Pleasure	Warm and comfortable
Relief	Fidgety
Guilt	Enjoyable tastes
Being carefree	Feeling full

Of course, this is not a complete list! However, it is a good place to start. None of these things are strange or unusual. They are all part of everyday life. Emotions and sensations are with us all the time. If you did a good job of recording your eating and activity habits, you will have noticed this. What you may not have noticed is how they are affecting you.

For a long time, **Jackie** thought that she knew a lot about her emotions and weight loss. However, she had never thought about positive emotions before and was surprised by what she found out:

"It was certainly helpful for me to think about more than negative emotions and eating (although I have certainly got stuff going on there!) It's now quite clear to me that positive emotions spoil my activity plans. I have tried so many times to start going back to the gym, but it has never worked out for me and I've never been able to understand why. I used to be really good at sport when I was at school and I used to love it. However, I think that this is exactly the problem. When I go to the gym I get really excited and enthusiastic (there's the emotion!) and I throw myself into the exercise expecting that I can do a lot. Of course, I can't do what I could do 20 years ago and I quickly get upset and disappointed, and

I give up. If I could make sure that my enthusiasm doesn't carry me away, I could make more sensible gym plans and would be more likely to stick at it."

Jackie had not really noticed before how her enthusiasm affected her. This is one of the problems with feelings. We all know how easy it is to slip into a bad mood without even noticing it – or even to find yourself eating something from the fridge without remembering how you got there!

So, emotions and sensations are perfectly normal and are happening all the time. How do they become a problem for weight loss and how can you tell which ones to focus on?

When do emotions or sensations become a problem?

Sometimes, the answer to this question is easy. If feeling sad makes a person eat a lot more than planned, that could well be a problem. If someone's plans to exercise are always spoiled by feeling tired, it is time to look at that feeling. However, people often do not know the complete range of feelings that affect them.

It helps to check out different possibilities. Have a look at the list below and think hard about your day-to-day life. Not every emotion or sensation will be a problem – indeed, most will probably have nothing to do with eating or activity. However, put a tick in the box if that feeling spoils your plans in any way – either through eating more food or less healthy food or taking less activity. You can also add any other feelings that are important to you but not on the list.

Emotion or sensation	Makes you less active	Makes you eat more (or eat less healthily)
Sadness	☐	☐
Fear or anxiety	☐	☐
Boredom	☐	☐
Anger or frustration	☐	☐
Happiness	☐	☐

Emotion or sensation	Makes you less active	Makes you eat more (or eat less healthily)
Resentment	☐	☐
Pleasure	☐	☐
Relief	☐	☐
Guilt	☐	☐
Being carefree	☐	☐
Hunger	☐	☐
Tiredness	☐	☐
An empty stomach	☐	☐
Cravings	☐	☐
Feeling sick or dizzy	☐	☐
Pain or soreness	☐	☐
Warm and comfortable	☐	☐
Fidgety	☐	☐
Enjoyable tastes	☐	☐
Feeling full	☐	☐

This is a good start in thinking about feelings and weight loss. However, it is not always more food – or less activity – that is the problem. Sometimes feelings can also make people use unhelpful weight-loss plans, in particular extreme plans. Here are some examples:

- Feeling bad about body shape, so going on a rigid "crash" diet.
- Not eating breakfast because of feeling a bit sick in the morning.
- Doing too much exercise because of feeling bad about missing a session.
- Not eating for many hours because of not feeling particularly hungry.
- "Banning" sweets or chocolate because the cravings are so difficult.

Jackie's example is a good one – her excitement about exercise made her *more* likely to exercise, but it led her to use an extreme plan that she couldn't stick to. She was not being Realistic about her goals.

To look at the issue of extreme plans for yourself, look at the table below. Again, think about your everyday life and think about each feeling in turn. Remember, there may not be any on this list that apply to you – and there may be lots that are *not* on this list that are very important. If so, write them down.

Emotion or sensation	Makes you use extreme activity plans	Makes you use extreme eating plans
Sadness	☐	☐
Fear or anxiety	☐	☐
Boredom	☐	☐
Anger or frustration	☐	☐
Happiness	☐	☐
Resentment	☐	☐
Pleasure	☐	☐
Relief	☐	☐
Guilt	☐	☐
Being carefree	☐	☐
Hunger	☐	☐
Tiredness	☐	☐
An empty stomach	☐	☐
Cravings	☐	☐
Feeling sick or dizzy	☐	☐
Pain or soreness	☐	☐
Warm and comfortable	☐	☐
Fidgety	☐	☐
Enjoyable tastes	☐	☐
Feeling full	☐	☐

Try to be sure about what is – or isn't – a real problem

When you have finished filling out this table, go back over it and check it. However, it is easy to make mistakes at this point. Because everybody knows about "comfort eating" and other such ideas, it is easy just to say "Aha! I eat more when I'm bored! This must be the cause of my problems." Well, maybe, but maybe not.

Think about your life. Suppose that you spotted that you ate more when you felt sad. What would that mean exactly? Would you just eat an extra big plate of pasta once in a while? Or would you end up snacking on big bags of salted nuts every evening for a couple of weeks? The extra pasta might not really be much of a big deal. However, lots of high-fat nuts on a regular basis would probably be important. Remember, Amounts Count.

Also, was there ever a time when you were overweight but did not really have these feelings much? And was there ever a time when you had these feelings but were not overweight? It is important to think hard about this, because if you put your effort into trying to change something that isn't that important, you could waste time and it might not affect your weight loss.

Don't be overconfident

Jackie was confident that she knew what her problem was:

> *"The main cause of my weight problem is comfort eating. After Craig was born I was miserable for a while. I ended up being stuck in the house and I tended to eat to make myself feel better. Well, that habit has stuck with me ever since and I have been overweight ever since. There is no doubt in my mind that comfort eating is the cause of my weight problems."*

Jackie might well be right. However, there are a few questions that we can ask. Certainly, she started being overweight and comfort eating at the same time. However, here is a list of other things that also changed at that time:

- She stopped work.
- She stopped being so active at work (she had previously been a nurse, on her feet all day).
- She stopped walking to and from work.
- She stopped eating lunch in the staff canteen.
- She started eating from the cupboards in her house.
- She started snacking on food that was in her house.
- Her sleep pattern – and due to this, her eating pattern – changed.

Can Jackie really be sure that it is definitely comfort eating – and *only* comfort eating – that led to her being overweight? What if she is wrong? What will happen if she spends a great deal of effort in trying not to comfort eat and she is actually missing part of the picture? She will waste a lot of time and effort and will probably fail to lose weight.

It is easy to be overconfident here and to think that we know all about our own habits. However, as we saw in Chapter 3, we often don't have a good picture of our own behaviour. Remember that plenty of "healthy weight" people sometimes eat a little more when they are upset or skip exercise when they can't be bothered. Many people who have no weight problems at all will stay in and watch the TV when they feel warm and comfortable and then start snacking when they are bored. These habits are very real, but they are *not causing those people to have weight problems*. Equally, just because an overweight person eats more when they are upset does *not* necessarily mean that this is a big part of their weight problem.

You have to be smart at this point, and make a judgement about how much of a difference an emotion or sensation makes. Work out what really matters in your life – and what doesn't. Here's how to discover what's really going on.

The Truth about your Feelings

The more you analyse and understand your feelings, the more you will be able to see how they affect your life and then do something about it. You may have spotted a large number of emotions or sensations that get in the way of your plans. However, you won't be able to deal with them all at once. It is best to choose one or two to work on – certainly no more than three.

There are two basic questions here:

1. What are the feelings like? For example, what triggers them? When are they most likely to happen?
2. What happens when you act on the feeling?

When you can answer these two questions, you will know how to treat your problem feelings.

Emotions and sensations often affect we do, even if we are not aware of them. So the first step is to become aware of how your emotions and sensations work. You need to become familiar with them. This may take a couple of weeks or so.

You can decide for yourself how you are going to get to know your feelings. You may already have a good idea about some of them from the recording that we covered in Chapter 3. However, you probably need to know more. These are the kind of questions that you need to be able to answer at this point:

- What makes the feeling happen? What are the "triggers" for this feeling?
- When or where do they happen most?
- What makes the feeling stronger? What makes it weaker? Think about all of the times that something has made the feeling go away.
- Are there times and places when you have this feeling but it does not spoil your plans – that is, you don't act on it?
- Has this feeling always been present? Have there been times when it was not there?

Once you have more of an idea about how feelings come and go, you will be able to consider what happens when you act on them:

- What happens after a feeling makes you do something?
- Do you really feel better after doing what you felt like doing?
- If you did feel better, for how long?
- Did you feel anything else about what you did – then or later?
- What effect did acting on your feelings have on your health – and feelings – in the long term?

Here are **Pete's** responses to some of these questions:

> *"Well, some of it is fairly obvious. I eat more because I'm in a good mood and I'm just delighted by the sight of good food and big portions! It's also obvious that I enjoy the food at the time and later feel over-stuffed. So I feel good at the time and terrible later. To be honest, I probably spend more time feeling terrible about my weight than I do enjoying the food. And the truth is that I will be fatter if I keep doing it in the long term, and my health will suffer. However, it's not the same all of the time. With some friends and some people from work, I won't overeat, even though I see exactly the same food in front of me and I have just the same feelings. So I guess I have some control over it."*

What do your answers tell you? Although everyone is different, most people find that neither their feelings nor acting on them are that helpful. It is important to remember this.

Feelings need to be put in their place

How do you usually treat feelings? How do you feel when they are happening? Probably that they are quite important. They feel like an important signal to do something or to avoid doing something: "I feel hungry – time for a snack" or "I feel tired – I probably shouldn't go to the gym."

So, feelings seem important and seem to offer good advice. However, they are getting in the way of your plans. So are they really offering good advice? Who is in charge here? If you make a good plan and decide to follow it, why does a feeling get to wreck it? It ought to be put in its place!

Acting on these feelings makes things worse

Look at your answers to the questions above, particularly at the questions about how acting on your feelings really makes you feel – and how it affects you for the long term. Most people find that feelings can promise a lot – for example, a sad feeling might promise that eating something will make you feel better – but when they think hard about what actually happens, they find that these are empty promises. A tired person who regularly lies on the couch rather than exercises will not make themselves less tired by doing this. Instead, they will get more tired as they become more unfit, and if they end up dozing on the couch their sleep pattern will become messed up, making things even worse. The promise was worthless – the opposite is happening.

However, sometimes what the feeling says is true. It is, however, usually only part of the truth. For example, comfort eating can make a person feel better – for a little while. However, they may also feel guilty or sad that they are overeating again, or appalled when they look in the mirror the next day and remember what they ate. The feeling forgot to mention this.

It is important to be realistic about what happens when you act on your feelings:

1. It usually doesn't work – it does not make you feel better
2. If it does make you feel better, it only does so for a short time
3. There are usually lots of other feelings that come along too – guilt, shame and hopelessness, for example.
4. Even if acting on the feeling does "work" for a while, it usually leaves you with more of your original weight problem – a problem that can be a serious long-term difficulty.

Do not let your feelings lie to you. They will tell you that the most important thing right now is a bit of pleasure from some food, or a bit of rest rather than some exercise. Of course, there is nothing wrong with either of these things once in a while. However, if you keep acting on your feelings it may seriously interfere with your weight-loss plans and leave you with an even worse problem to deal with.

Emotions and sensations come and go

The truth is that emotions and sensations often don't give very good advice and they are not as important as they may appear.

How to Do It

When you look at the emotions or sensations that are causing you trouble, you will probably see that they come and go depending on what is happening around you. For example, a person might have a really strong craving for chocolate, but then the phone rings. During the conversation, the "really strong" craving just vanishes.

Will these feelings come again in the future? Almost certainly. Will they go away again? Yes, certainly. All emotions and sensations are temporary.

You can ignore them and put up with them

Something else to bear in mind is that you have a good record of ignoring or putting up with emotions and sensations. Look at your past – there will have been plenty of times when you will have done something even though you were anxious or not eaten when you were hungry. Have you ever feel angry but chosen not to act on it? Have you ever faced a challenge even though you didn't feel confident? There are probably many times when you have done something when you did not feel like it or when you haven't done something despite a strong urge!

Who is in charge here?

So, emotions and sensations are not as important as they say they are, and not as powerful either. They are temporary and you can put up with them. Remember this, because otherwise *you are being pushed around.* If you decide on a plan and an emotion wrecks it, then you are being bullied.

In Chapter 1 you spent some time deciding what your reasons for weight loss were. These reasons are important and personal. They can get you through hard times. They are far, far more important than any emotion or sensation. Feelings will come and go – reasons won't. Aren't your reasons more important than a passing sensation?

You Are in Charge of your Plans – Not your Feelings

Hopefully you now have some idea of which emotions – good and bad – affect your plans. Clearly, if you want to lose weight you may have to deal with some of these issues. This book *can* help you to stop feelings affecting your weight-loss plans. However, it *can't* help you get rid of any unpleasant feelings that are causing you trouble.

This is a really important point. If a person has a problem with feeling sad and this makes them overeat, it might seem sensible to try to get rid of the sadness. However, sadness is a normal part of human life. So are anger, fear, boredom, tiredness, hunger and lots of other feelings. Nobody can get rid of them. Of course some emotions can become a serious problem. If this is the case, check out the books in the "Overcoming" series on dealing with difficult emotions. These will provide a good starting-point. There is some more useful information in Chapter 9. Here we will simply deal with the *impact that feelings have on weight loss.*

In most cases the best way to deal with this is to learn how to experience all of the emotions that we listed above – because they are all natural and normal and we will all experience them again anyway – but to make sure that they have no effect on your eating and activity plans. Here is how to do it.

Name them

You now know that it is important to put feelings in their place. This does not mean getting rid of them, or thinking they are untrue, or just "in your head" – but it *does* mean remembering that they are just feelings and may not be as important as they say they are.

Here is a fun exercise in seeing feelings for what they are. The first step is to choose one of your difficult emotions or sensations and give it a name. It will be much easier to deal with when you can call it by its name. However, it is important to have a little fun with the name to remind your feeling that it is not as important as it thinks it is. This is *not* an exercise that is designed to make fun of *you* or your situation, but it is trying to make fun of some *feelings* – particularly the ones that are making things difficult for you.

Pete, for example, noted that his sheer pleasure in big quantities of food made him eat a lot when he was in a good mood. He decided to call his feelings "Homer" after Homer Simpson, the doughnut-eating hero of the cartoon *The Simpsons*. Pete swears that he can sometimes hear Homer shout "Woohoo!" when he sees a big plate of food.

Jackie was aware that she started to snack when she was too busy and felt stressed. She decided to call these sad feelings "The Hungries". She says that during these moments she is definitely hungry for *something* – but she is usually hungry for a rest or a bit of company, not food. Calling these feelings the Hungries reminds her to think about what she is actually hungry for.

Kirsty found that she was very unlikely to go out and get some exercise when she was back in the house after work and feeling warm and comfortable, and this was messing up her activity plans. She decided to call these feelings "Mrs Adventurous". She found this a good way to gently poke fun at the feelings that kept her on her couch.

You can play around with some names and use the ones that work best for you. Next time you have the feeling, it will be much easier to spot whether Homer or Mrs Adventurous is around.

Look at the thoughts that go with them

In Chapter 2, we noted that strong emotions or sensations almost always bring thoughts with them. We have also seen how feelings tend to promise things. However, there are many more types of thought than promises. For example, if Pete noticed that Homer was around when he was out for dinner ("Woohoo!"), there would also be thoughts along the lines of "More dessert! Who cares? I'll worry about losing weight tomorrow."

Below are a few examples of thoughts that go with particular emotions and sensations. They are all in some way biased, unhelpful, or present a limited view of the situation. Look at this list and imagine what would happen if you just believed them without questioning them – how would it affect your weight-loss plans?

Sadness

"I need something to cheer me up."

"Nothing else fun is going to happen, so I may as well eat something."

"There's no point exercising – it will never work."

Pleasure

"I need to allow myself *some* pleasures!"

"You only live once. It's better to enjoy this than worry about dieting."

"I don't want to exercise. I want to have more fun."

Anger

"It's not fair that I should have to change my eating and exercise."

"People who stare at me are idiots. I'm not going to go out and let them mock me."

Hunger

"I'm not full yet – I need some more."

"I'm hungry. I need some food."

"This is awful. I can't bear it."

Cravings

"I won't be able to concentrate until I have eaten this."

"There's no point fighting it – it doesn't work."

"I'm just addicted to chocolate – it's best to accept it."

Tiredness

"I need to rest."

"If I do that I will be exhausted."

"What an idiot. How can I stick to my plans when they behave like that? I might as well not bother."

"I need a snack for energy."

Boredom

Warm and comfortable

"I may as well have a snack to break up the time."

"I deserve a rest."

"Exercise is boring – I can't be bothered."

"I don't want to make my life any harder than it already is."

"All of this new food is boring – I can't be bothered."

"Going out on a day like this will be horrible."

It is fairly easy to see how these thoughts will help feelings spoil your plans. However, *who is in charge here – your thoughts or your reasons?* If thoughts are getting in the way of your plans, then deal with them. You know what to do with unhelpful thoughts. Go back to Chapter 2 if you have problems remembering the drill. We will go over it briefly here:

- First, spot the thoughts that seem to go with the strongest feelings. Then write them down in a way that:
  Explains the most important part of the thought.
  Summarizes it briefly.
- Then you can then go on to:
  Question the thought.
  Expand it.

If you do a good job of questioning and expanding the thoughts that go with your feelings, you will reduce the power of your feelings to spoil your plans. Also, you may find that it makes the feelings less strong overall. This is a good bonus. However, remember what the main goal is: to keep going with your plans no matter what feelings are there.

Hunger, Fullness and Being Upset

Whatever happened to trusting your body?

Sandra has a problem with some of these ideas. She believes in eating healthy, natural food and being in harmony with her body:

> *"This is weird. Why are you putting things like hunger and tiredness on the same list as being bored and sad? People need to listen to their bodies more. When a person is hungry they should eat, and tiredness means that they need some rest. You should be encouraging people to trust their bodies."*

She is making a very sensible point. If hunger, for example, were a good indication of needing food, it would be smart to pay attention to this feeling. However, it is important to do some hard thinking about feelings like "hunger" and "tiredness".

Many people do not feel hungry when they wake up in the morning. Why not? After all, they may not have eaten anything for 12 hours. In general, we are all most "food-deprived" first thing in the morning. Yet many of us do not feel hungry. If hunger is a signal that the body needs food, then what is going on?

Similarly, some people can't understand why they are tired even though spend a lot of time resting. But, as we saw earlier, resting and not getting enough exercise can mess up our sleep patterns. So if a person listens to their feelings and decides that feeling tired means that they need to take it easy, this will only make things worse.

It is certainly true that all people in the Western world feel the need for food regularly. We desire food, have cravings for food, feel a kind of "emptiness" in our stomachs and feel "hungry" before meal times. We have cravings for sugar or for big bulky meals that will fill us up. Yet most of these feelings have nothing to do with the body having a real biological need for food. Most people in the Western world are lucky enough to be overfed.

So your feelings of "hunger" or "tiredness" are not necessarily good friends giving good advice. However, they are not your enemies either. There is no point completely ignoring them, or trying to "beat" them. It's better to understand them:

- Your feelings of "hunger" or "tiredness" may – or may not – have nothing to do with what your body needs.
- If you are following good, balanced (non-extreme!) eating and exercise plans then these are probably a better guide to what is good for you than your feelings of "hunger" or "tiredness".
- This may mean that sometimes it is smart to eat when you *don't* feel hungry or to exercise when you feel tired. Stick with your plan and you will be on the right track.
- Hunger and tiredness are just sensations, like any others. If they are getting in the way of your plans, remember this. They will pass.

Holding Steady

Naming emotions and sensations is helpful. It is useful to get to know how and when they come and go in your life. Also, dealing with the thoughts that come with them is often a very helpful step. However, even if you do these things, you may still be left with unpleasant emotions and sensations that seem very strong. They may still affect your eating or activity plans. How do you deal with this?

It often seems easier to give in to emotions or sensations. Sometimes it is. If you have a craving for something sweet, you may just want to eat it so that you can concentrate again and get on with things. It is important to be honest about the fact that giving in can be a relief. In the long term, though, it will only make things worse. And there is one other important rule that you should know:

Giving in to emotions or sensations often makes them stronger

Giving in to cravings can be like pouring fuel on a fire. There are lots of reasons why this might be the case, but here are a couple of examples:

- First, giving in to feelings gives you the idea that they are in charge. It makes you feel less in control. This will make you more likely to give in next time.
- Second, the relief that you feel is a strong positive feeling. Indeed, it is a much more pleasant feeling than trying to resist your feelings. This tends to keep the habit of giving in going.

The good news is that the opposite is also true. Refusing to give in to feelings – or "holding steady", as we will call it – can make the feelings weaker. This reminds you that you are in charge, not the feelings. However, it is not always easy. The next section shows you how to do it.

Holding steady – how to do it

When strong emotions or sensations are present and telling you to do something they can feel very powerful. It often feels as if they will carry on forever or keep getting worse and worse if you don't give in to them. Indeed, perhaps you have tried to "hold steady" in the past and it has not worked. In this situation, it seems easier – and smarter – to avoid struggling with the feelings.

However, this is *not true*. Cravings, for example, cannot last forever – they are just feelings, after all. The same goes for anxiety. Feelings can certainly be very unpleasant and can feel destructive, but in fact they only become destructive when you act on them. This whole exercise is aimed at breaking the link between unpleasant feelings and the negative actions that they can cause. It is important to hold this in mind when you are "holding steady".

There is one main truth about holding steady: *if you keep doing it long enough, then the feelings get weaker (and sometimes even go away)*.

Here are some good ways to get through this process:

1. Keep your reasons in mind.
2. Remember what really happens when you act on your feelings.

3. Keep doing things – carry on living your life (but don't run away from the feelings).
4. Keep naming the feelings, seeing them for what they are and spotting the thoughts that go with them.
5. Keep going and hold steady. Don't do what you feel like doing. You can keep going longer than the feelings can. You are in charge!

These five steps are explained in detail below. However, it is important to pick the time and place when you are going to practise this. As it can be quite challenging, it is best to choose a time when you are less stressed than average and when you have a bit of time on your hands. Holding steady can feel like a bit of a battle at times, so start by choosing times when you are likely to win. That way you will get into the winning habit. Here are the steps in detail.

Keep your reasons in mind

Whenever you are going to do something difficult in weight loss, it is wise to have your reasons in mind. Holding steady can be a tricky business, so keep them in mind now. You will probably end up holding steady through unpleasant feelings like anger or cravings. You will want to get rid of those feelings or give in to them. Your reasons will give you the strength to "hold steady" through them.

Remember what really happens when you act on your feelings

If your feelings have a bad effect on your eating or activity, remember this when you are holding steady. If they set you back and make things worse, remind yourself of it. Keep doing things – but don't distract yourself.

Keep on doing what you were doing when the feelings came up. It is important to keep on living your life. It is not that easy to "outlast" feelings of sadness and boredom if you are sitting alone in a dark room. Keep active.

However, it is very important that you do not use activity to distract yourself from the feelings and run away from them. The point of this exercise is to show the feelings (and yourself) that you can hold steady and outlast them. It is important to show who is in charge.

Keep naming the feelings
A feelings is just a feeling. It can be unpleasant, but remember, it's just Homer – or Mrs Adventurous. It is easy to lose sight of this when a feeling is strong, but if you keep naming them, then you will keep putting them in their place.

As for thoughts, particularly ones like "I can't stand this" or "This will never work", remember they are unhelpful and biased. Treat them in the way they deserve.

Keep going and hold steady
If you hold steady for long enough, then the feelings will get weaker. You might have to hold on for quite a long time, but this is *always true*. Feelings can't last forever.

In many ways, holding steady is a waiting game. You may have to practise it a few times and you may need to use your problem-solving skills to adapt it so that it works best for you. However, if you hang on long enough it is a game that you will *always* win.

An important health warning

Although it may seem simple, holding steady is actually a very powerful psychological technique. However, it can be used for the wrong things. You should only use it when you are sticking to a sensible, balanced, healthy eating and exercise plan. If you are using an extreme weight-loss plan like a rigid diet or a very intense exercise plan, then *you should not be using this technique*. If you are following an extreme plan then your feelings of hunger or soreness or anxiety may be telling you something important. This technique is useful for one thing only: dealing with the feelings that stop a person having a moderate, sensible eating and exercise plan. Do not misuse it.

What to do when emotions are difficult
nearly all the time

For most people, negative emotions can be painful, but they are not a problem all the time. There are good days and bad days, but there is always light at the end of the tunnel. Unfortunately, some of the time emotions like sadness, anxiety or guilt become a serious problem on their own.

When strong and painful emotions are present most of the time, they may need treatment in their own right. If they are beginning to seriously interfere in your life, then it may be time to consider getting some outside help to deal with them. There is no perfect way of working out when to get help. However, if you find that your life is being seriously disrupted by painful emotions and there is nothing that you can do to help yourself then it is time to get some help.

Getting help for emotional difficulties makes sense in the same way that consulting a doctor about a medical problem or a financial advisor about money makes sense. There is no shame in it. It does not mean that you have failed or are a weak person. Serious emotional problems are just things that happen, like the weather. In some places, at some times, the weather gets intense and a little scary, and it is the same with emotions. It makes sense to consult an expert at these times. In Chapter 9 there is some information on seeking professional help, finding a good therapist and using medication.

Food is Marvellous and the
Couch Feels Great

We have talked about a lot of different emotions and sensations and explored how to stop them getting in the way in the way of weight-loss plans. However, one thing has been missed out.

Think of the satisfied feeling that comes after a big meal. Or the beautiful taste of some food. Think of how good it feels to decide to stay on the couch when the weather is bad. Let's be honest, this all feels great!

Food is one of the great joys of life. This is absolutely the right way to see it. It is not "the enemy". Also, it is not a disaster to skip activity or exercise once in a while. Again, it is a pleasure to have a warm house, a comfortable couch and a decent TV. When thinking about weight loss, it is important not to get values out of place and start to think that food and/or a bit of comfort and idleness are bad things. They are not.

You are aiming to lose weight so that you can be healthier. If you are healthy, you will live a longer life with more energy, less pain and discomfort and fewer medical worries. If you are healthy, you will be free to enjoy more food – in moderation – for longer, and with less worry and fewer complications. The same goes for activity and exercise. It is not much fun if your couch is comfortable but every time you climb the stairs you get out of breath. The fitter and more active you are, the more you will enjoy your moments of relaxation. You will sleep better, have less physical discomfort, your mood will be better and you will take demanding activities in your stride.

So eating healthily and exercising are not about taking the pleasure out of life. They will bring *more* pleasure to your life. This is the deal: you will lose some "pleasures" in the short term, but will have more pleasures in the long term. We think that this is an honest way to look at it. Whether you agree – and whether you want to take this deal – is up to you.

Summary

- Notice how emotions and sensations affect your weight-loss plans.
- Find the most important ones, name them and get to know how they affect you.
- Hold steady – don't do what you feel like doing – and the feelings will fade eventually.
- Get help if your feelings are a serious problem.
- Don't forget that food and rest are *not* your enemies.

8

Dealing with Other People's Reactions

"Things got so much easier when I moved out of the house I was sharing with friends. We all tended to eat together and pick up each other's habits. As soon as I moved out it was so much easier to eat healthier food in more sensible amounts."

"I know that I need to change my habits. The trouble is, so does everyone else! How am I going to manage if my husband, kids and friends all carry on eating and sitting around like they did before?"

In an ideal world, your weight-loss plans would be not be influenced by other people. Of course, this is not that easy! Other people can have a great effect – either positive or negative. However, this chapter can show you how to deal with the challenges.

First of all, it is important to work out all of the different ways in which other people are affecting you. Then you will know what you need to deal with.

How other people can influence weight loss

There are lots of different ways in which other people can influence weight loss. To make things simpler, we will deal with two general areas.

First, *other people's choices can affect your choices*. For example, your housemate may choose to fill the fridge with tempting unhealthy food or your partner might insist that there is not enough money to afford gym membership. In one case you have an extra choice – unhealthy food – and in the other case you have one less choice – going to the gym. In both cases, other people have affected what you can and can't do. This can feel like a hopeless situation – people often feel trapped when the people around them are not helping.

However, sometimes other people can affect your plans *by the way that they treat you*. They can encourage your plans to lose weight or they can be negative, perhaps saying that your plans will never work or avoiding you when you are trying to lose weight. Sometimes complete strangers are openly nasty – for example, laughing when you try to exercise for the first time.

Here we will deal with these two areas in turn. First we will help you to analyse all of the ways in which other people affect you. Then we will cover the skills that you need to deal with these situations.

Other People's Choices Can Affect your Choices

Jackie is thinking about the things that would make weight loss just a little easier:

> "Well, if I had my choice, it would be like this. I would have a private gym in one room of my very large house. And a personal trainer, of course. I would have a fridge full of healthy food. I wouldn't buy it, because I would have my own personal dietician to pick it all out for me. And I'd have a personal cook to keep an eye on the portion sizes. Also, if I ever wanted to go out, to an exercise class, for example, then I would have someone around who could look after Craig – childcare is important . . . If I went out of the house, I would make sure that I wouldn't go near any fast-food outlets, or shops that sell snacks, or anywhere else that might cause trouble. Hang on, I'm sure I can think of some more things . . ."

All this would certainly make weight loss a great deal easier! However, most people's lives are far more complex – and full of other people who can affect weight-loss plans. Your partner, family, friends, workmates, boss and total strangers can all affect your plans. The people who run big food businesses, the diet industry and your local shops can certainly affect your plans – the people who want to persuade you to buy food are a big influence on everyone in our society.

All of these people generally affect you in one of two ways – either they *change your environment* in some unhelpful way or *you rely on them* for some things and they aren't helping. Let's look at these in turn.

Other people change your environment

Your environment – the things that you have around you, or don't have around you – really matters. As mentioned in the introduction to this book, the epidemic of weight problems in the Western world has been due to changes in the environment. None of us are immune from these influences.

Personal surroundings can often have a bad influence. Here are some examples:

- Your partner insists on having unhealthy food that you find hard to resist in the house.
- You need to have snacks or treats in the house for children or visitors.
- Family or friends bring round unhealthy food and it seems rude not to have some.
- You stay with family or friends and they feed you unhealthy stuff.
- Your "treat" to your children is to take them to a fast-food outlet.
- When you go out with friends, they choose restaurants with unhealthy food or insist on ordering unhealthy food to share.
- Your colleagues always have a tin of biscuits in the office.
- There are vending machines with chocolate and crisps close to your desk – a lot closer than the canteen or the nearest food shop.

- Your desk has a computer and a phone, so you never really need to leave it apart from to go to the toilet.
- You have a job that needs you to stay in one place – inactive – a lot.
- You go out with friends to pubs and bars that only have unhealthy food.
- You have to go shopping with children who beg for unhealthy food.
- Your family is in the house watching a movie – with some great food – when you are planning to go out and exercise.
- The fast-food outlets near your home offer no healthy options.
- Some places offer free samples of food.
- In many shops near your home, there are chocolate and crisps easily available near the checkout.

Obviously, there are many, many ways in which other people's choices affect yours. This is just a short list.

How does your environment spoil your plans for eating and activity? Think in turn about the different environments that you find yourself in. Have a look at the list below. Write down the main thing in each environment that messes up your plans.

Environment	This messes up my eating plans	This messes up my plans to be more active
Home		
Work		

Environment	This messes up my eating plans	This messes up my plans to be more active
Friends' houses		
Family's houses		
Restaurants, or other eating or drinking places		
Other places when you are out and about		
Places on journeys that you make – for example to and from work, picking up other people		

Do not worry about filling every box – this is just meant to help you think about these issues in an organized way. Later, there will be some ideas that about what you can do about these difficulties. Now let's look at another way in which people can affect you.

Other people do not give you practical support

It would be a lot easier to change activity and eating habits if you could do exactly what you wanted all the time. However, most people cannot do this. You may have people who rely on you – children, for example, or other relatives. You may also rely on other people, for example on your partner to help out with things around the house. This becomes very obvious when people who want to be more active decide to take some structured exercise. Here are some examples:

- You need your partner to look after an elderly relative whilst you get some exercise.
- You need people to cover at work whilst you take a walk at lunchtime.
- You need your partner or family to agree on money – for the gym, for example, or for clothes or equipment for exercise.
- You need someone to give you a lift back from the gym in the evening when it is dark.
- You need someone to look after your kids so that you can shop without them nagging you for unhealthy food.
- You need someone else to do the shopping so that there is food in the house and you don't end up having to have fast food instead.
- You need someone to do their share of the household chores so that you can have the time to exercise.

There are many more examples like this. Later on, we will cover how to deal with these issues. For now, it is important to understand how they work in your life.

First of all, think of all of the situations where other people set back your plans by not helping. Think first about your plans for activity and then about eating. Ask yourself:

- Which parts of your current plans are difficult and sometimes fail because other people will not (or cannot) help?
- Which of your plans have failed completely in the past because other people have not helped?
- Which plans have you never even tried because you have always assumed that you could never get the support from other people?

These are the problem areas: write them down. Secondly, work out:

- Who is not giving you the practical support – partner, friends, colleagues?
- What exactly do you need them to do? Try to be precise.

Again, write these things down.

These are some of the practical ways in which other people can make weight loss difficult for you. However, there are other ways in which they can affect you which are less clear but can matter just as much.

How Other People Treat You

People encourage you – and discourage you

You may have a friend who encourages you to go out for a long walk each weekend. You may have another friend who tries to get you to go on "crash" diets with her. You may have a neighbour who mutters abuse at you in the street or a housemate who is nasty about your weight-loss plans behind your back.

We do not need to worry about the positive influence that other people have (though don't forget to thank them once in a while!), but the negative influence can be very difficult to deal with. Some people are just horrible – those who laugh at you in the street, for example – but others may be responding negatively because they are confused by what you are doing or take it personally somehow. It is obvious that weight can be a very sensitive issue. If you try to lose weight, it may make others feel uncomfortable, and they may act in a way that is not helpful for you. It is important to note that we are talking about the *effect that other people's behaviour has on you*, not judging other people or analysing what they are trying to do.

Think about your activity and eating plans. Who has a strong effect on them? Specifically, which people cause you to break your plans? Think about the following sets of people:

- partner
- family
- friends
- people at work
- strangers

Write down who seems to have a big effect on you. Remember, this does not mean that they are *trying* to be unhelpful; it is just an exercise in being honest about the effect that other people have on you.

People encourage extreme plans

We have often noted that an extreme weight-loss plan – whether diet or exercise – is as bad, if not worse, than no plan at all. Even if you have moved away from using these methods, this does not mean that everyone around you has. Friends or workmates may still be keen on them and may encourage you to join them or be openly doubtful about your more moderate approach. This is important. If friends do affect you like this, write this down.

People try to help in an unhelpful way

When other people support weight-loss plans, this can be really helpful. Also it can be very annoying. Here are some examples of close friends and family who are trying to help someone lose weight, but probably doing the opposite:

- "Are you sure you should be eating that?"
- "You have missed your exercise class twice this week. You will never lose weight like that."

- "You don't need to lose weight – you look fine to me." (This was the partner of someone who was clinically obese and at a high health risk.)
- "Good morning! It's another beautiful day. What can I do to help you with weight loss?"
- "Of course, if you want to exercise, you will need a decent pair of running shoes. Those ones are no good. And I can give you some good advice on training schedules . . ."
- "I'll just make you a green salad for your evening meal – that will help, won't it?"

You can see what is happening, can't you? Most of us do not like to be monitored or have the idea that someone is checking up on us. Someone who is regularly trying to "help" can seem like a spy with a video camera! Also, other people's advice and attempts to help make it can seem as if they are trying to control you. Many people will rebel against this by doing the opposite! This is understandable – but unfortunately it can ruin perfectly good weight-loss plans. Again, if there are any examples like this in your life, write them down.

So far, we have covered the things that people directly *say* or *do* to you. However, there is another way, even harder to see at times, in which other people affect you: they affect you by influencing your attitudes.

Other people affect what seems "normal"

Nobody in any society is born knowing *what* to eat and *how much*, or how much exercise they should take to stay healthy. However, most of us go through our lives thinking that we know what is "normal". In fact, all of our ideas are learned from other people. We see what our parents ate and how active they were, and this has a strong influence on us. Later in life, friends and partners come to have more and more of an effect. Yet we forget all this and end up thinking that our own beliefs are "obviously" the "normal" way to do things. In fact, they are just what happens to be in our own heads at that moment.

What is a "normal" level of activity and exercise?
To get an idea of what we mean, look at the following questions about activity.

- Is it "normal" to take the stairs or the lift? Is it "normal" to walk somewhere or take the car?
- Is it "normal" to use a bike to get around (or just plain dangerous)?
- Is it "normal" to take regular exercise or to avoid it?
- Do "most" people take active holidays such as walking or "inactive" holidays like sitting on a beach?
- Is it "normal" to always take a shortcut or to walk a little further?
- Is it "normal" to accept the offer of a lift or to politely refuse because you need your walk?
- Is it "normal" to have exercise equipment at home or to own sports clothes? Or is it "normal" to think that people who enjoy exercise are a bit weird?
- Is it "obvious" that running can damage your knees?

Whatever your answers to these questions, they are not "common sense" or "what normal people do" – they are in fact *beliefs and thoughts*, like those we discussed in Chapter 2. Most people do not spend much time questioning these beliefs – partly because they don't often question any of their beliefs and also because it is easier to see things as "normal" when *lots of people around you are doing these things*. Indeed, in a small way, for the people around you some things are "normal". Of course, this does not mean that they are healthy. For some people, it is "normal" for their friends to be overweight and unfit.

It is a very good idea to look at what you think is "normal" for exercise and to realize that these beliefs mainly came about because of other people, not because you consulted an expert and were told that they were healthy.

What is a "normal" style of eating?
The same points apply to food and eating:

- What kind of portion size is "normal"?
- Is it "normal" to have a dessert?
- How many times a day do "normal" people eat?
- How often is it "normal" to have a snack between meals?
- How often is it "normal" to have fast food or takeaway food?
- Is it "normal" to crave chocolate?
- Is it "obvious" that some people can be addicted to chocolate?
- Is it "normal" to usually buy a snack when you go into a shop?
- Is it "normal" to need a "treat" a few times in a day?

Kirsty certainly noticed how this had an effect on her:

> *"A few years ago, I was living in a shared house with friends. It had a huge effect on my weight. Very often we would sit down in an evening as a group and watch a film together. When we did this, it was just obvious that we would order pizza and have a few bowls of crisps lying around. One day I just woke up and realized what I was doing – a couple of times a week, I was completely stuffing myself. Of course, nobody has to have a whole pizza whilst watching a video! But at the time, it just seemed like the thing to do – it had become a habit. I am more aware of that kind of thing now."*

Pete also had a moment when he realized what he was doing:

> *"I have to travel quite a bit with my job and I end up doing quite a lot of driving. In the past, whenever I stopped to get fuel or have a break I would get a snack at the same time, usually a chocolate bar. I used to look around me and see other people – slim people – getting a snack too, so I thought it was just what people do. Of course, I realized later that other people do not always get a snack every time they stop for fuel or a break – they just do it occasionally. But I thought that buying something every time was just normal."*

Both Kirsty and Pete were being guided by thoughts and beliefs about what was "normal". Also, because other people around them were supporting these beliefs, it was not easy to question them and see them for what they were – just beliefs, not necessarily the truth.

Other ideas that can seem normal

The final important type of belief is a bit more general. It is usually an attitude towards eating or exercise that has been passed on through a family or culture. Some of these may seem familiar:

- What it comes to exercise, it's a case of "no pain, no gain".
- You should never waste food – there are people starving in the world.
- Always clear your plate.
- It is rude to refuse the food that people offer you – you are being polite to your host by eating it all up.
- Some people are cut out for exercise and some people aren't.
- If you refuse the food someone offers you, then you are rejecting them.
- Everyone who exercises is some kind of gym-mad nut who doesn't know how to enjoy life.
- If it is in your family to be overweight, then that's the way it is going to be – no escaping it.
- People who turn down food are being snobby and rude, trying to pretend that they are better than other people.

Most families have some "rules" like these and it is easy to see how these ideas can affect weight loss. However, it is also important to see that they are just ideas and not necessarily the "truth".

Check That your Problem Is Really What You Think It Is

By now you will have looked at a number of ways in which other people can affect your weight-loss plans. Hopefully, you have been writing things down and now have a list of areas where things are difficult. It is time to work on solutions to these problems.

To summarize, we have covered four different types of problem:

1. People change your environment in a way that makes weight loss harder.
2. People don't give you practical support when you rely on them.
3. People encourage and discourage you.
4. People may make unhealthy eating and activity habits seem "normal".

This is a big range of problems and a few different ideas and skills will be needed to deal with them. However, first it is useful to ask a few questions. Earlier, we saw that people tend to presume that their view of a situation is the truth and seldom spend much time checking whether they are right. It is worth checking that your view of your problem situation(s) is completely accurate. If there are other, more helpful ways of seeing a situation, it is worth spending time to find them. Things that seem like a serious block could look very different from another angle. You could use the question and expand skills from Chapter 2 for this. Here we have focused on a few key issues.

Check your facts

It is obviously important to check your facts when it comes to a belief about "normal" eating and activity. How would you know? How many "normal" people have you asked? Have you asked some people who are a healthy weight? And even if you do come to the conclusion that your habit or belief is normal, is it healthy?

Check your facts too when it comes to your "problem" situations. For example, if you have identified a way in which someone does not give you important practical help, is it really impossible to do what you want to do without their help? Have you really thought through all of the ways in which you might manage on your own? If you have not gone through some systematic problem-solving on this issue (*see Chapter 6*) then you do not actually know what you might be able to manage on your own.

Similarly, if other people's discouragement – or encouragement – is blocking you, is it really true that if they went away one day things would be perfect? Have they always ruined your plans or have there been other times when you have stuck to your guns? If you have, is the current situation really all their fault?

It is always easy to blame other people. However, the truth is often more complicated. The purpose of "checking your facts" is not to blame *you* for everything or to make you feel guilty. However, if the problem lies partly in you as well as in others, then this is actually *good* news. You have more control over yourself than you have over other people. It means that you can start to change right now, by working on your own habits.

Be honest about mixed feelings

Many people have their weight-loss plans spoiled by others encouraging them to eat more than they had planned to. Whether it is their grandmother giving them an extra portion or their friends buying them a dessert, this can be a problem. However, be honest – if you were in this situation, would you be completely unhappy that someone had bought you a dessert? Or would a bit of you be quite pleased?

It can be very useful to be honest about mixed feelings like this. Once you start to be honest with yourself, you can start to think about what you really want – in the long term, as well as the short term. You can make clear decisions about what is most important for you.

How to Do It

Check that you have really told people what you want

As we noted above, it is easy to think that other people are to blame for not helping. However, are you sure that you have really asked the people involved to start helping – or to stop what they are doing? Think about this seriously. Have you asked them in a really direct, clear way that makes it absolutely clear in concrete terms (*see SMART, Chapter 6*) what you want them to do?

If you want to check for yourself, think about the last time you raised the issue. Write it down or imagine it from the other person's perspective. Imagine that they were a little tired or distracted when they heard it. Imagine that they did not really think that it mattered much to you. Did you manage to express yourself in a way that was completely clear and impossible to get wrong? Probably not.

Let's look now at how to communicate in a way that is clear and forceful but respectful – and effective.

Deal with the People Involved – Raise the Issue and Negotiate

You may have decided – after checking your facts – that there really is a problem with another person. Something what they are doing is getting in the way of your weight loss. If this is the case then you need to ask them to behave differently. Simple, isn't it? Of course not. Imagine saying to your friends: "Please could you stop suggesting that we go for chips on a night out. Instead, please could you accompany me to a salad bar?" You probably wouldn't get very far . . .

There are a couple of important truths about dealing with other people. First, it is clear that you will not be able to control anyone else's behaviour. People will do what they like, and you cannot directly change that. However, you *can* change the way that you communicate with them. You can seriously influence how likely a person is to listen to you by how you approach them and what you say.

Usually, people do not handle these "difficult" conversations very well. They tend to do one (or more) of four things:

1. Avoid the issue and not mention it at all.
2. Raise the issue, but then give in as soon as the other person disagrees.
3. Get angry or yell at the other person.
4. Grumble, mutter, be sarcastic or try to give the person "hints" about what they should be doing.

Pete has tried all of the above.

> "Ann often buys in food that I just can't resist. I hate it when there is ice cream in the freezer. Of course, part of me loves it too and I really don't seem to be able to resist eating some when it is around. I haven't really talked to Ann about it – apart from last night. Generally, I just avoid the topic. I've tried to drop some hints – not very clever really, I'd just say something like 'Oh, ice cream again – that's nice and healthy!' She never seemed to get the message, but I guess that's not surprising. I got more and more fed up about the situation. Finally, last night, I flipped – started yelling at her, telling her that she should be more considerate and try to help me with my weight loss, not sabotage it. It was awful. I made her cry and I feel like a horrible person."

Kirsty has had no more luck:

> "I often go out for a drink on a Friday with my work buddy Celia. She is great fun and we have a good time. However, there is always a point in the evening when she says, 'Let's go for a pizza!' I know Celia well – when she has got her mind on something, nothing is likely to change it. I usually just groan to myself and go to the pizza place, promising myself that my healthy eating plan can start again next week. I have tried to persuade her to go somewhere else, but she says, 'That's boring! Let's go for a pizza!' and I never know what to say. I just end up following her."

How to Do It

None of Pete or Kirsty's efforts have gone very well so far. However, these conversations are not easy. You need to do many things at once – stick to your guns and get your point across whilst being calm and respectful towards the other person. You also need to be very clear and able to talk about how the situation makes you feel. There is quite a lot to think about, so we will take it a step at a time. The first step is to clear your head.

Clear your head

Before you start having your difficult conversation, you need to check that your view of the situation is not going to get in the way. Use the skills from Chapter 2 and catch your thoughts about the situation. Pinpoint them, explain and summarize them. Watch out for thoughts about the other person ("They are doing it on purpose!" "They don't care!") and about what is fair and unfair in the situation ("How dare they!") Here are some examples from Pete and Kirsty's situations:

> *Pete:* "My main thought is 'She's so inconsiderate!' There is also 'She doesn't care about my health' and 'She doesn't listen to me.'"

> *Kirsty:* "It's something like 'There's no point, she won't listen.' Also some thoughts about her: 'She's just a good-time girl, she won't really care and she'll probably think I'm boring.'"

Remember that these thoughts may be untrue or unhelpful. We often make judgements about other people even though we know nothing about how they feel or how they see things. We also never know exactly how our own behaviour looks to others and how it might affect them.

So notice your thoughts and then put them to one side. You might be right, but you might not. You do not know the other person's side of the story. Your judgement may be wrong. Focus on the things that they are *doing* that are causing you problems, rather than on your opinion of their *character*.

The second part of "clearing your head" is becoming clear about what you want to get out of the conversation. You need to think this through in advance. The authors of a helpful book on this topic, *Difficult Conversations* (*see Appendix II*), imagine what it would be like if NASA scientists were to say: "Well, we'll just launch the rocket up towards space and then see what happens – we'll take it from there." This may sound obviously impractical, but many people do start off their difficult conversations like this!

If you want another person to do something differently, then you must be prepared to give them a clear example of what you would like them to do. For example, does Pete really want Ann never to buy in ice cream ever again under any circumstances? Even if they have guests or on special occasions? He needs to think this through in advance. If he cannot tell Ann how he wants things to be different, then he cannot complain if she does not get it right. It can help to use the SMART principle here (*see page 132*). Be prepared to give the other person some Specific, Measurable examples of how you would like them to change, ideas that they have some chance of Agreeing to and that are Realistic and on a Timetable.

Pick your moment – then start talking about the situation "from above"

Pick your moment

When you have some idea of what you want to achieve, you can think about raising the topic. Only you can decide when it is a good time to start a difficult conversation, but here are a few guidelines:

- Try to leave yourself plenty of time for the conversation.
- Try to pick a time when neither of you is too stressed.
- Don't "ambush" the other person – the idea is to have a real conversation with them rather than to force them to agree with you quickly or embarrass them in front of others.

There is probably never a perfect moment for some conversations – just try to pick a relatively good one.

Talk *"from above"*

The next principle is to start to talk about the situation "from above" – as if you were seeing the other person's behaviour *and* your own behaviour from the outside. This is important because when we are not happy with another person's behaviour we can usually only see our side of the story. However, this is no way to start a conversation. Imagine if a friend came up to you and said: "I don't know why you are being so inconsiderate! What you are doing is so hurtful that you really have no excuse . . ." Would you really feel like listening to the rest of what they had to say? So step away from your personal point of view and talk about the situation as if you were an observer.

Here are some good rules for starting the conversation:

- Talk about the situation as if you were observing it from the outside.
- Talk about facts and behaviour, rather than your opinion of the other person's character.
- Make it clear that this is your point of view – and that you might have got it wrong.
- Say something positive about the other person and acknowledge that you have also contributed to the problem.
- Talk about yourself and how you feel, rather than judging the other person's behaviour and character.

Pete is doing a great job of using these ideas:

> "Ann, my love, I have been thinking about the food that we buy for the house. I know that you deal with all of that stuff – it's a lot of work and I really appreciate you organizing it. However, I'm really stuck with something. I'm still struggling with my weight and I am lousy at resisting ice cream when it is in the freezer. I would really like it if we could avoid having it in the house – or at least just have it in once in a while. It would make a lot of difference

> to me. I know that in an ideal world I would just be able to restrain
> myself and not eat it. But that doesn't seem to work like that at the
> moment. I'd really appreciate it if we could change what we buy –
> it would mean a lot to me and help me out. What do you think?"

Here Pete is speaking "from above" as an observer and then
speaking clearly about what he wants.

The next example shows how he might do it if he were ignoring these guidelines:

> "Ann, I have been thinking about the food that we buy for the
> house. It's really annoying me. I need you to start thinking a bit
> more about my needs. You know that I have real problems dealing
> with ice cream when it is in the house, but you will carry on buying
> it. I'm not quite sure what your problem is, but you need to get
> this clear in your head: no more ice cream – OK?"

In this situation, Pete is being calm and stating what he wants,
but he is not saying it in a way that Anne is likely to be interested in listening to. Ask yourself if you honestly respond well
when people speak to you in this way. Also, which approach
will start a conversation? Which will encourage Ann to speak
to Pete and perhaps even tell him things about his own behaviour that he does not realize?

Of course the second example is forceful and clear – and
these tactics might get results if they are used with someone
who is easily bullied. However, they are a bit like the techniques used by a salesperson trying to push you into buying
something. They might succeed in getting you to make the pur-
chase, but you know that you will go away feeling a bit manipulated and you won't want to go to that shop again. If you ever
do, you will *listen less to that salesperson next time*, maybe even
avoid them. You may not want this pattern to develop in your
own relationships. Instead, imagine how you feel when you talk
to a salesperson who really explains all of the products available, does not pressure you and really seems interested in your
requirements. You will seek them out the next time you are in

the store and will listen to their advice. In the long term, they will probably be more persuasive. Many people prefer this kind of pattern in their relationships.

Ask for help and listen to what the other person has to say

The idea is to start a useful conversation and to state your own wishes clearly and directly, not to bully someone. This will not only produce a better long-term atmosphere in your relationships but also have a number of immediate benefits. It makes the other person feel that you value their opinion and are interested in what they have to say. This will make them more likely to respond positively. Also, you are more likely to learn something. Remember, the other person may have information that can help you.

You may notice that Pete ended by saying "What do you think?" By doing this, he is inviting Ann to get involved in the discussion. He is saying to her – though not out loud – "I care what you think, and I would appreciate your opinion and help." This is a good first step. However, the next step is more important: you must be genuinely willing to listen to what the other person has to say. This means being prepared to consider changing your view about a situation. This is important. If you listen but do not really hear, then you will learn nothing. Also, the other person will notice.

Here are a few quick rules about what other people can tell about you in difficult conversations:

- They can tell when you are not really listening to them.
- They can tell when they are being bullied and manipulated.
- They can tell when you have already made up your mind about something and are not seriously considering any other alternative.

However, if you are genuine, then people are likely to tell you their point of view and help out.

Pete decided to grit his teeth and really listen to what Ann had to say:

Ann: "I really didn't think that it mattered that much. I mean, whenever we have ice cream in the house, you eat it! I thought that meant you liked it . . ."

Pete: "But you know I'm trying to lose weight. And I don't exactly look pleased when I see you have bought some, do I?"

Ann: "Sure. Of course, I noticed you looking a bit grumpy. Then you would usually start eating it! I thought, 'If it really matters, he'll say something'. And you never did. Until now."

Pete: "Oh."

Ann: "I'm not really that keen on ice cream. It's usually you that finishes the carton. I don't mind not getting it."

Pete has probably learned something from this conversation. It is clear that relying on Ann to "guess" how he feels about food is not good enough. Also, this conversation showed him that his thoughts about the situation – that Ann was inconsiderate and didn't listen – were completely wide of the mark. She was paying close attention to his behaviour all along. However, he was not communicating clearly.

Of course, difficult conversations do not always go as well as this. They are usually a lot more tense. In the situation above, Pete is not asking Ann to make much of a sacrifice, as she doesn't really like ice cream. When the other person feels that they do have to sacrifice something, they will sometimes try to resist you. This can take a few different forms, such as:

- ignoring you
- treating what you say as unimportant
- changing the subject
- making it all into a joke
- implying that you are being selfish
- giving lots of reasons (excuses) why they can't do it

- saying that they didn't *mean* to be unhelpful (and therefore that their behaviour is OK)
- arguing
- simply refusing altogether

All of these things are difficult to deal with. Most of us hate getting into arguments. Also, it is easy to start thinking that you have got it wrong when the other person is being forceful or persuasive. In these situations, some extra techniques are needed.

Talk about yourself clearly and forcefully

Kirsty's friend Celia is a bit more of a handful than Ann. Here is Kirsty's first attempt to talk to her:

> *Kirsty:* "Listen, Celia, I know we usually go for pizza at this point in the evening, but I'd really rather try something a bit more healthy. Instead, we could go to . . ."
>
> *Celia:* [cutting in] "Come on, you know that you want to!" (laughs)
>
> *Kirsty:* "But maybe this time we could . . ."
>
> *Celia:* [cutting in again] "Oh come on, girl, it's getting late! Friday night is pizza night. Get your coat."
>
> *Kirsty:* [speechless] . . . [gets her coat]

It took Kirsty quite a while to get up the courage to have this conversation and afterwards she felt hopeless about the whole thing. She wondered how she would ever manage when Celia would not even let her finish her sentences.

In situations like this:

1. Talk about yourself and your feelings.
2. Be very clear and concrete about what you want to happen
3. If you get into a discussion or negotiation, be clear what your "bottom line" is, so that you don't end up agreeing to something useless.

4. Repeat yourself. State your point of view again. And again. And again. (The "broken record" technique.)

Here is Kirsty putting these ideas into action:

Celia: "OK, it's time for some food! Let's go."

Kirsty: "Seriously, Celia, this evening I want to go somewhere other than the pizza place."

Celia: "Oh come on, Kirsty, you know we always go for a pizza!"

Kirsty: "I know we have in the past, but . . ."

Celia: [cutting in] "It's getting late, let's go."

Kirsty: "Celia, this matters to me and I need you to listen to me now. I would like to go for some food that is more healthy than pizza."

Celia: "This is all about your weight, isn't it? I wish you would just accept that you are a beautiful woman the way you are."

Kirsty: "Thanks, Celia, but it's about my health as well, and my health matters to me. I would like to go somewhere different this evening."

Celia: "God, you're really hung up on this, aren't you?"

Kirsty: "This is important to me. I'd like to go somewhere else."

Celia: "OK, let's go some other place next time . . ."

Kirsty: "No, I would like to try somewhere else this evening."

Celia: "Alright, alright! You're kind of scary this evening! I give in. Do you have somewhere in mind?"

Here Kirsty has used the "broken record" technique very well. She said that she wanted to go to a different place *five times*. Eventually, Celia realized that she would say it 25 times if necessary, and decided that she had better listen. This is the beauty of the "broken record" technique. It makes it clear to other people that you will say the same thing no matter how they try to distract you or argue with you.

The second important point is that Kirsty just talked about herself – she mentioned what was important *to her* and what *she* wanted. She did not get into a conversation about how Celia wasn't listening or helping. It is important not to start accusing other people or labelling their behaviour as unhelpful. Here are the reasons for this:

- Whilst you are talking about yourself – what matters to you and what you want to happen – you can *only be right*. Nobody knows you better than you do, so it makes it hard for the other person to argue.
- On the other hand, if you start accusing the other person and labelling their behaviour and their character, they can (sometimes with reason) disagree and start an argument. You are no longer on solid ground. Also, you will offend people and make them less likely to listen to you.

There are, however, some mistakes that you can make when talking about yourself. For example: "I've been feeling that you're a selfish, stupid pig who never listens!" This sounds direct and open. It may also be honest. It might make you feel better about getting it all off your chest, but so would throwing a plate at the other person – and neither would be a very mature or smart move. Imagine how you would feel if someone said this to you. Would you get the impression that they wanted to start a constructive conversation? Would you be more or less likely to make an effort for them?

So, when you are trying to have a difficult conversation, you need to talk clearly about yourself, but you also need to watch out for any urges to tell people what you really think of them or to really let them have it. People who do this usually come across as arrogant and unlikeable. This may not bother you – but it will certainly ruin your chances of managing the conversation well.

Here is another way of managing the same statement – without mentioning the words "selfish, stupid pig"(!):

> *"I have been getting upset and I've been finding it hard to know what to think. From my point of view, I have tried to raise this issue with you a few times. However, I do not think that we have ever had a good talk about it and I have never seen you suggesting a way that you can help. You are generally the kind of person who is happy to help with something like this. Perhaps I have not been making clear how much this matters to me. It really does matter to me. Can we talk about it right now?"*

How would you feel this time if someone said that to you?

Difficult conversations are certainly not easy. You have to have several different things in your head. For example, you must be willing to negotiate, but have an idea about your "bottom line" and be willing to stick to it. It's hard. This is why so many very smart people still have difficulties talking to their relatives – or to their bosses, or to salespeople! You can explore this topic more by looking at some of the books in Appendix II. But meantime it is worth practising the skills. If you wait until you feel confident before having a go, you will wait forever.

However, there is one other big block that stops people from getting started:

Feeling guilty and selfish in difficult conversations

If you are having a difficult conversation, this usually means that you are talking about things that are important to you and are asking other people to change their behaviour in some way. This often triggers thoughts like:

"I'm being selfish."
"I shouldn't put myself first – I should be thinking of others more."
"They will think that I am a horrible pushy person."

If this happens, use your skills from Chapter 2. Look at the thoughts and beliefs that flicker through your head when you are having these conversations or when you are thinking about having them. These thoughts are just thoughts and are not necessarily true or helpful. Use your question and expand skills here.

When you are having a difficult conversation, you are not doing anything very radical. All you are doing is saying something about yourself and your health. It is something that you have thought hard about and that you have decided is important to you. You are just asking the other person to listen while you tell them about a way in which they could help. You are willing to listen to their point of view. You are not yelling, throwing things, bullying them or threatening them. So *how can doing this be selfish?* The answer of course is that it is not selfish, it is just clear communication about something important. If the other person thinks that is selfish, then that is their problem, not yours.

Many people think that they should consider others' needs and try to put other people first. These are good beliefs and can make a person kind and considerate. But surely if you are considerate and listen to other people, then you too have the right to be listened to and shown consideration. Your needs are as important as anyone else's. And the more you look after your own health and emotional well-being, the better you will be able to care for others. There are plenty of overweight people out there who have sacrificed their health for their families because they believed that family came first. Of course now their families have to look after them because they have weight-related health problems and cannot do what they used to do. There are no prizes for ignoring your own needs.

Toughen Up – and Sort It Out on your Own

Unfortunately, having a well-planned and well-managed difficult conversation does not guarantee that you will get good results. It makes good results more likely, but sometimes people will still ignore your needs, and there are some other people you will simply not be able to negotiate with at all.

If you get into trouble with your difficult conversations, you will probably be having one (or both) of two difficulties:

1. You are not getting practical help from the other person.
2. The other person is being discouraging or abusive.

We discussed practical support above. Abuse can take a few different forms. Here are some examples:

• open verbal abuse such as calling you names
• scorn and contempt
• teasing and making fun of you
• undermining you and saying negative things about what you are capable of
• saying abusive things but making it sound like "a joke" or "fun"

These can be very upsetting and destructive. They can certainly spoil someone's well-planned weight-loss efforts.

There are two steps for dealing with these issues. The first is to think practically.

Try to sort things out on your own

This is the obvious first step when you are not getting the practical support you need. If this is your problem, try thinking about the issues using your problem-solving skills from Chapter 6. For example:

• If you need your partner to look after an elderly relative whilst you get some exercise, could someone else cover for you?
• If there's no one to look after your kids while you exercise, could they come with you?
• If your partner won't give you a lift home from the gym on dark nights, could someone else do it?

Obviously, there are no simple solutions to the difficulties that you listed, or you would not have listed them. But remember, you never know how close a solution is until you start looking for it!

It is also a good idea to start with practical solutions when other people are being negative or abusive. For example, when **Sandra** goes for a walk she finds that local kids on the street yell abuse at her and call her names. There may be practical options here, for example:

• Are the kids there all the time? Could she go out when they are usually away?
• Is there some way of checking whether they are there or not before going out?
• Are there any other routes she could take?
• Could she go out once or twice with her large and scary-looking brother-in-law?

It is always worth checking that you have covered all of the practical options. However, even good problem-solving does not guarantee an answer. You may still be left in a situation in which people are negative or abusive towards you and spoiling your weight-loss plans as a result. You may not be able to change the abuse, but you can change how you respond to it.

Toughen up

Most of us come across rudeness and abuse in our lives. Some of the time this really hurts and some of the time it is not too bad. The type of abuse matters and some people are more able to hurt us than others. Also, it depends on how we are feeling on that particular day – some days we can shrug things off and some days everything hurts. A lot depends on how we see the situation – that is, on what our thoughts about it are. If we change our thinking, we can change how things affect us.

The thoughts in Sandra's head went something like this:

"I thought if I went out during the day, no one would see me . . . They are so cruel, just picking on anyone who looks different . . . I hate the fact that they can see me sweating and my body wobbling as I walk along . . . I just can't handle being abused on a daily basis . . . How dare they? How do they have the right to treat me like this?"

There are a few different types of thought here: thoughts about the other people and thoughts about Sandra herself and her ability to cope. When we are upset by abuse, our thinking often runs along these lines.

If you have a situation similar to Sandra's that is making you upset, use your skills from Chapter 2 and pinpoint the thoughts. Try to summarize what is most upsetting about the situation. You already know the procedure for dealing with these thoughts. You can get going right now, using your question and expand skills. Below are some questions that can help you:

- Questions about the other people:
  Why are they doing this? What exactly is their problem?
  Why don't they have anything better to do with their time than be rude? Are their lives really that dull?
  Why do they feel so uncomfortable about me taking steps to lose weight?
  How do they have the right to judge me? Are they particularly special or talented?
  If I decide not to be affected by these people, are they really able to hurt me? If I decide to ignore their words, how much can they hurt me?
- Questions about yourself and your ability to cope:
  Why do I have to meet some kind of standard or be some particular way to be acceptable? Why do I have to "pass" someone else's "test" to be OK?
  What does my size have to do with my character or my quality as a person?

Don't I have a right to do what I like, walk where I like, lose weight how I like? So long as it does not hurt anyone else, don't I have the right to do what I like? If they don't like it, they don't have to pay any attention to it.

Do I want to let these irritating people spoil the quality of my day? Do I want to let them spoil my plans?

How many other irritating and stupid people have I dealt with in my life? If I have dealt with them, why can't I deal with this lot?

Do I know anyone else – either personally or a fictional character – who has put up with a lot of rudeness and abuse but kept going and kept their pride? What can I learn from them?

Sandra went through this process and ended up feeling a little differently about her situation:

"I ended up thinking of the local kids as a little bit like flies – small, mildly annoying creatures that are hard to get rid of. However, they are creatures without much brain that can't really get in my way and are only a minor annoyance – certainly not worth getting upset over! I noticed that they only do it in a group. Whenever I pass one of the kids on their own, they don't say a thing. That says a lot about why they are doing it and about how brave they are . . . I guess I also got a bit of my pride back and held my head up a bit more. I still did practical things – I still try to go out when they are least likely to be around! – but I have taken a serious decision about whether I will let them stop me doing what I want. Fourteen year olds are not going to get in the way of my plans."

In Sandra's case, the problem did not go away, but changing her attitude towards it improved both her feelings and her ability to get on with her plans.

However, even if a person changes their thinking about a situation, this may not completely take away the shame, sadness or anger that they feel when another person treats them badly. So it is useful to decide what to do with these emotions.

Are you willing to have the unpleasant feelings?

Difficult situations create unpleasant feelings. Look at Sandra's situation. She felt embarrassed, humiliated, angry, upset and ashamed. What would have happened if she had decided that these feelings were so awful that she would not accept feeling them under any circumstances? She would never have left her house again!

Similarly, if any of us decided that we could not bear to feel anxiety, stress or fear, we would never leave our homes – or even our beds! Unfortunately, it is true that other people can make us feel unpleasant feelings and that they sometimes decide to do so on purpose. There is not a lot that we can do about this. However, how we treat the feelings can make a huge difference. The whole issue can be summed up in one sentence:

So long as you try to avoid the unpleasant feelings that other people can cause you, then they control you.

For example, if you never want to feel upset and angry, then you will never confront another person about an issue – and that means that they control you. If you never want to feel embarrassed, then you will probably never try out new exercises or activity in public – and this means that other people are controlling your behaviour, rather than your own plans.

On the other hand, the opposite is also true:

The moment that you decide that you can put up with the unpleasant feelings that other people give you, then they no longer have any control over you.

If you decide that you will raise an issue with someone, even though it will make you tense and angry, then you are in charge. If you decide that you will go swimming, even though you feel embarrassed in a swimsuit, then you are in charge. This is a bit like the exercises in "holding steady" in Chapter 7. You will not be able to get rid of bad feelings altogether, but you can change how you treat them. Feelings are not as powerful and unbearable as they say they are – and when you decide to accept them and experience them anyway, they often lose their power.

Summary

- Check how other people affect you – both in practical ways and in how they treat you.
- Don't take your view of the situation as the automatic truth – check it first.
- Raise difficult issues with people when you can – but think about when to do it and how to do it skilfully.
- If this doesn't work – or if there are people you can't negotiate with – find ways to toughen up and carry out your plans anyway.
- Your reasons for weight loss are important and you can find ways to move toward them with or without other people's help.

Keeping It Going

"I've made some great changes so far. Let's hope they last."

"I think I have been here before – I've been given lots of good ideas and then left to keep going – for the rest of my life, on my own!"

This book started by pointing out that managing weight in the long term is difficult. It is. This is because you need to change your eating and activity habits *and then keep those changes going*. Weight loss is more like a distance race than a sprint. You need to make a plan that will "go the distance".

Over time a lot of things can change in people's lives. Jobs change, relationships change, moods change – and you need a plan that will see you through it all. It is best to be realistic – on your way to weight loss, you will probably come across some of these situations:

- You might slip with your plans but hardly notice it, then suddenly realize that you have gained quite a lot of weight.
- You may get stuck and feel as though there's nothing you can do.
- You may find yourself going backwards.
- It may be hard to know when to keep going and when to be happy with what you have achieved.
- After trying for some time, you may realize that you are dealing with a serious problem with your emotions.

Don't panic – you can actively work through all of these difficulties. This chapter will give you practical, positive ways of doing so. It will also cover the scientific research on why people stop sticking to their plans.

How to Stop Things Just Slipping Away

It is easy to stop thinking about something without even noticing that you have stopped. For example, most people have suddenly had the horrible realization that they have forgotten about something – like an unpaid bill – for a very long time. This can happen very easily with weight-loss plans – a person can let their eating habits slide then suddenly become aware that they have started to put on weight, for example, or they might stay the same weight but not notice that their exercise programme has stopped.

This tendency to forget is a fact of life. We do not seem to be designed to carry out long-term projects. Of course, sometimes people can keep focused for months or even years. People can study for an academic qualification for years, but there are usually other people – for example, teachers – around to keep them going, and there are particular goals that they need to achieve on the way, for example exams. However, with weight loss, you may be faced with the need to keep going for quite a while without any help from other people or any external goals to keep you on track. And it's human nature to let things slip away. Scientific research shows this very clearly – it is very common to see people lose weight for six months and then for the weight loss to begin to stop.

Clearly, you are more likely to keep going if you have a plan. Just deciding that you will "try to remember and keep track" will probably not be good enough. There are two useful steps that can help here. The first is to look at any mixed feelings you may have about carrying on with your weight-loss plan. Second, there are some practical ideas that can help.

Check your thoughts about the long term

If they are honest, many people find the thought of having to think about food and activity in the long term rather boring and difficult. As with most mixed feelings, it is best to be honest about this. Stop for a moment and imagine having to keep an eye on eating and activity for the next five years of your life. Try to pinpoint (*Chapter 2*) the emotions and the thoughts that go along with this idea. You may find some thoughts like:

"It's all such a huge effort."
"Five years without being able to relax . . ."
"This is miserable – where's the fun?"
"It will be a process of starving and restricting myself."
"No way. You can't make me do it. I'll do what I like."

Try to pinpoint your own personal thoughts about this. Then you can use your question and expand skills to check that these thoughts are fully true and helpful. Taking the examples above, how much effort are we talking about exactly? And maybe you do want to relax, but are you relaxed right now about being overweight? How relaxed would you be if your health got worse? Do you find going to the doctor relaxing? Very often, people think of continued weight loss as someone trying to control them or spoil their fun. Is this the case? And anyway, don't you have your own important reasons for losing weight?

Remember, the aim is to make sensible, reasonable plans that you can imagine sticking to in the long term. These plans should not be extreme or restrictive. And ultimately, being healthy may be just as much fun as being overweight or under-active, if not more!

If you spend a couple of minutes with your notebook looking at your thoughts and seeing how balanced they are, it will be time very well spent.

How to Do It

Make some appointments

Once you have considered carefully any mixed feelings you may have, you will have a better chance of success with your plan. However, you will still need a prompt once in a while to check that you have not lost track of where you are. Reminders are always helpful.

So you need to make some appointments. The first type of appointment is an appointment with yourself. This may seem a little silly – you may think that you already have quite a lot of your own company. However, we are talking about booking serious quality time to do something useful. How much time do you really spend on your own, undisturbed, focusing on something that's important to improving your own health and well-being in the long term? Exactly – that's why you need to book an appointment with yourself.

Schedule in some appointments to check on your progress – perhaps one a month. It is wise to book a few in a row. Also, have a note next to the last booking that reminds you to book some more! If you do this, you have some time to check on your own progress and see how you have been doing. If you wish, you can use the space to do some problem-solving about issues that are still difficult.

Of course, you will need a diary or a calendar to make this work. If you do not have one, the best move is to get one and to start using it. However, if this really does not work for you, there are other ways. **Sandra** has an example:

> "I have never used a diary and I'm not about to start now. However, I need about three appointments with myself for the next six months. I've decided that I will check in with myself at Easter, then the day after Don's birthday and finally before our summer holiday. Three appointments, no diary."

Apart from yourself, it can be equally useful – sometimes more useful – to book appointments with other people. The most obvious person could be your family doctor. You can sometimes book months in advance and could ask them to remind you to report about what's happening to your weight loss. Of course, friends can do this too and with a commercial weight-loss group you can check in when it suits you.

Whoever you choose, make sure it is someone who will be friendly and supportive. This is not meant to be a check on whether you have been "good" or not. It is meant to be a way of keeping track and checking in with yourself.

Getting Stuck and Going Backwards

As well as having plans to make sure your weight-loss plans don't slip from your mind, it is important to think about how you are going to react when things go wrong. If you are reading this book, then there is a good chance that you have tried to lose weight before and it has not worked. It is also clear that, once in a while, even with good plans, things will still go wrong and you will get stuck.

Responses

Getting stuck – when nothing is working and you can't see the right way forward – can be upsetting. It can lead to feeling hopeless and frustrated. Even worse is going backwards – many people have experienced the nasty business of not only losing weight but actually gaining it. However, what you need to do in these two situations is the same.

Two things will happen when things go wrong. First, you will have some thoughts about the situation. Your mind will certainly have a view on what is happening and what that means about you, weight loss and the future (and it probably won't be very positive). Second, you will react on the basis of these thoughts.

What you actually do at this point can be more or less helpful. The following will be very unhelpful:

• Giving up. Starting eating and exercising according to old habits.

- Deciding to stop trying for a while – a week, a month, a year . . .
- Trying very hard not to think about the whole issue of weight loss and health.
- Feeling miserable and doing nothing.
- Starting to search for new magic cures or new medical opinions.
- Blaming someone else and stopping trying to lose weight "until they change".
- Going back to using extreme or fad diets that only work in the short term.

All of these reactions are quite understandable – they make perfect sense, given the circumstances – but the main problem is that they will not get you anywhere.

Some recent research shows which responses are the biggest problem. The researchers took a group of women who had just finished a CBT weight-loss programme and asked them to keep diaries of the times when they were tempted to drop their weight-loss plans and the times when they actually did. Interestingly, the number of temptations did not seem to matter. The only thing that made the women more or less likely to give up their plans was *their response to the temptations*. Women who thought that a minor setback was a real disaster tended to fail the most. However, when they managed to use some kind of "coping" response, they kept themselves on track. There were many different types of coping that helped – the main point seems to be that people do well if they do *something* to help themselves.

The main message of this research seems to be that the power to keep on track is inside you – if you can find ways to cope with setbacks then you will be able to cope with most temptations. Here are some ideas on how to cope well.

A *positive response*

It is important to be realistic here. The first step in dealing with a setback is to accept that it is happening. If it is a serious setback, then it is definitely worth being honest about it.

Recall the two main responses to setbacks: thoughts about the situation and then actions. Both of these need to be managed.

Think ahead

First, it is a good idea to decide in advance how you are going to think about such situations. **Pete** decided to use the idea of weight loss being a distance race:

> *"The way I see it, weight loss is going to take me a long time. It's like a distance race – kind of like a marathon. If you watch marathon runners, you see that they are often not too bothered if one of their opponents passes them and goes in front. They know that this is a long race and there is plenty of time for them to make up the gap – or for their opponent to get tired out. They certainly don't panic and immediately think that they are going to lose! I have plenty of time . I'm going to keep on making sensible, moderate plans about my eating and exercise. I'll get there in the end, even with a couple of slips on the way."*

Have a think about how you would like to approach setbacks. If you work this out in advance, you are more likely to cope well. Some people use sayings like "Two steps forward, one step back" or "Don't make a mountain out of a molehill." See what you think might work for you. Anything will do, so long as it makes sense to you and will allow you to be calm and practical when things get difficult. Again, if you spend a few minutes with your notebook thinking about this *right now*, it will repay you in the long term.

Make the right moves

Second, it is critical to make the right moves when things are going badly. People often run into problems with this. We have noticed two main problems that happen to people who have some training in CBT:

1. They just get stuck in saying how awful it is. They are either not doing anything to help themselves or are relying on someone else to fix things for them
2. They start using plans that are miles away from CBT. They return to extreme diets or take up the latest fad diet that comes onto the market, or start using some unproven weight-loss supplement.

What is interesting about these people is that they do not use their CBT skills. Sometimes they think that because they are having problems that means that CBT does not "work", in the same way that their old diets did not "work". However, CBT is not like a diet, but more like a set of tools. Imagine that you are trying to build a house and it is not going well. There is no point getting upset, then sitting around hoping that the house will build itself. Also, imagine there is absolutely no evidence that there are any better tools around than the ones that you are using at the moment. (There is currently no evidence that any approach to weight loss is clearly better in the long term than CBT, apart from stomach surgery.) The smart move is to keep on trying to build your house using the tools that you have as well as you can. It might be difficult and need a lot of thought – and there is no guarantee of success. However, the other options are worse, and by carrying on with the job you will learn from your mistakes and refine your skills, thereby giving yourself a greater chance of success.

So the main thing to do when you are having problems is to *use your CBT skills*. This may sound like really obvious advice. However, as we have seen, people very often just do not do this. Remember, CBT skills can be applied to *any* situation. (Of course, they are not guaranteed to fix it, but what do you lose by trying?) Don't do them half-heartedly. Sit down with a pen and paper and do the exercises properly. There is a reason why many CBT exercises are quite "formal": *because they work a lot better when you do them this way.* Decades of experience have confirmed this. Don't ignore it. When you are stuck with your weight-loss plans, you might:

- Do some problem-solving.
- Check that your reasons and your motivation are clear and strong.
- See if any thoughts or beliefs are getting in your way.
- Record your own behaviour to check you are not missing anything.
- Make some new SMART plans.
- Check if any feelings – or other people – are getting in your way.

Problem-solving is probably the most useful technique in dealing with setbacks and, as we noted in Chapter 6, there is scientific evidence suggesting that regular formal problem-solving can help keep weight off. However, there is one final thing that you might need to do:

Check your facts

It is very easy to get some basic facts about food and activity wrong. If you do get something wrong – like thinking a food is healthier than it actually is – then you can get into trouble. Although many people are well informed about food, no one has a perfect understanding. If you do not have a degree in nutrition, then you should always presume that there is more to learn about the food that you eat.

Similarly, if you overestimate the amount of energy burned by a particular exercise, then you may be confused about why you aren't losing more weight when doing it.

It is wise to get some expert advice about the facts of food and activity. Consult a professional or some kind of resource that is likely to be reliable. Some are listed in Appendix II and there is also advice later on in this chapter.

Keeping It Going – and Knowing
When to Stop

So far, we have only covered the negative things you might encounter. However, it is also likely that at some point you will find yourself doing well. This is obviously very good news! However, it will bring its own challenges. For example, there will be times when weight loss has been going well but you have reached a decision point. Weight loss may have slowed down or the next move to lose weight may seem like a really big effort. There is a central question you will have to ask yourself: "Shall I keep going or shall I just stay at this weight and be happy with my progress so far?"

For many people, the answer to this question is easy: they will stop when they have reached their "goal weight" and not before. Many people have thought about their "goal weight", or their "ideal weight" for some time. Some have very strong dreams and fantasies about what they will do when they reach this weight. It becomes a big issue.

You may have noticed that the world of weight loss involves a lot of numbers. People count calories and they also measure their progress in terms of numbers – usually the weight they have got to or the amount that they are losing per week or per month. This approach has some good aspects. It is hard to cheat with numbers – a person has either lost weight or they have not. However, there are also some serious problems with the "numbers" approach to deciding whether to carry on losing weight. First, it is hard to know whether your goal weight is realistic (sometimes it can sound a bit more like a "fantasy weight"). Second, focusing on numbers loses the reasons why you are losing weight in the first place – the reasons that you worked out in Chapter 1.

How do you know if your goal weight is realistic?

Another way of putting this question is: how do you know how much weight you are capable of losing? In the long run, are you capable of losing huge amounts of weight? Or are you just one of those people who will never manage much, even with good CBT skills?

The answer, of course, is that you don't know – no one does. There is no way of predicting what you can do. Someone once asked the sprinter Michael Johnson how fast he thought he could run. Johnson replied that he had no idea and that he would know this when he had run all of his races. He refused to guess how much he could achieve – and by doing this he avoided placing any limitations on himself. It is a wise approach.

There are two important facts to bear in mind when considering how much you might be able to lose. They come from the NWCR study and also from studies of the outcomes of CBT programmes.

The NWCR study shows that people can lose very large amounts of weight, and keep it off, by themselves without any drug or surgery. This is the good news.

However, the CBT research is less good news. It shows that people going through good CBT programmes on average only lose about 10 per cent of their weight – for example from 15 stones to 13.5 stones, 210 lbs to 189 lbs, or 93 kg to 84 kg. They then tend to regain a bit of this weight over time. (Of course, 10 per cent is just an average; some people lose nothing, some people lose lots more than this. Also, 10 per cent is a good result in medical terms and will reduce the risk of disease.)

To summarize: *It is possible to lose large amounts of weight and keep it off. However, most people do not manage these large weight losses, even with good professional help.*

It is important to bear *both* of these facts in mind when thinking about how much weight you want to lose. This is why goal weights are a problem. They can be over-ambitious – or under-ambitious – and you would never know if they were. Look at these two people:

- One person loses 10 per cent of their body weight quite easily and then immediately stops. They say, "I have lost as much as most people in CBT studies. This is the best that people can do with professional help. Therefore it is pointless for me to try to lose more."

• The second person loses 20 per cent of their body weight but still does not get down to their fantasy weight and back into wearing the clothes they wore when they were younger. They are bitterly disappointed and become miserable.

Having a goal weight has tripped both of these people up. The first person has limited themselves unnecessarily while the second person is ignoring their superb progress.

It is also noticeable that goal weights are often very ambitious. One study found that people seeking weight loss had ideal weights that were so low that little short of stomach surgery would achieve them. We are sceptical of goal weights for these reasons.

However, another reason to avoid measuring progress in numbers is that numbers don't matter. Did anyone ever make a huge effort for a number? But your reasons from Chapter 1 really do matter. That's the real way to measure your progress.

Measure your progress by looking at your reasons for weight loss

If a person is losing weight for their own important reasons – for example to keep healthy for the sake of their children – will they be worried if their weight loss is slow (but sustainable)? However, the person who wants to get to their fantasy weight will be disappointed by slow progress. Which matters more, getting near to a number or achieving something important to you?

When you ask yourself whether to keep going with weight loss or not, you can help find the answer by looking at your reasons. The real question is *not* "Have I reached my goal weight?" but "Have I made good progress in doing what I set out to do, for my own important reasons?"

Remember that **Jackie** was hoping to get back to her job in nursing? She was also going to have more time to herself as her son became a teenager. She listed the following reasons to lose weight:

1. To develop herself by taking charge of her life in this area.
2. To safeguard her health (and to carry on indulging her love of food!) by lowering her risk for diabetes.
3. To make sure that she can keep up physically with her family on walking holidays.
4. To get into better shape in order to feel more comfortable in a senior nursing role.

Jackie made good progress in working towards these reasons. She became a great deal fitter and lost a good amount of weight – although not quite as much as she would have liked. Then she reached a point where losing more weight was getting harder and harder and she began to doubt whether she had the real motivation to keep going:

> "I realized that I had done really well in terms of my reasons. I had certainly taken charge of things and I was tracking my diabetes risk by checking the tables in some medical textbooks that I have. I'm at much less risk now. Also, my activity programme has involved a lot of walking and I'm now pretty sure that I walk a good deal more than Craig or John – they will have a hard time keeping up with me on our next holiday! Finally, I have no problems spending hours on my feet now, which matters from a nursing point of view. I probably won't have to do that kind of thing any more, as I'll have a more supervisory post, but I'll feel better about leading a team of nurses who do have to spend a lot of time standing. To be completely honest, I haven't lost as much weight as I would have liked. However, I've done the most important things and I think that is why my motivation was flagging – I knew deep down I had done what I needed to do. The 'beauty' and 'cosmetic' reasons never mattered to me, deep down."

Jackie has assessed her progress in terms of things that really matter – and she knows that she has done well. She would like to be slimmer but she also knows that "looking good" and "fitting into old clothes" are not serious personal reasons that will give her the energy to do this.

There is one final area where reasons are important. The good thing about reasons is that they are usually not concrete goals that a person can reach and then stop bothering about. For example, "staying fit and able to walk a long way" is not something that you can achieve and that's that – you have to keep it up. In an example from Jackie, "taking charge" of weight control is not a one-shot event but an ongoing attitude of mind. So your reasons can help you keep things going and keep good progress alive.

Staying at a particular weight and keeping good plans going can be a challenge

We have written a lot about losing weight and becoming more active. However, the main challenge is keeping weight off and staying active. Even if someone is content with the progress that they have made and has stopped trying to lose more weight, they may still need to make some effort to keep their gains.

When good progress has been made in weight loss and activity, it is important to turn your plans from weight loss to weight maintenance. If you are a person who has struggled with your weight for some time, then it is probably the case that you cannot simply sit around and be certain that the weight will stay off. You will have to work actively – though hopefully you will not have to work too hard – to keep it off.

Switching between being "on" and "off" a diet

People very often switch between being "on a diet", where they are paying lots of attention to what they do and making a big effort, to being "off a diet" where they are making no effort and trying hard not to think about the whole thing. This is not a great way to proceed for the long term. However, if you follow the advice above, for example by making regular appointments with yourself, you will be able to pay attention gently and constantly to your progress without making a massive effort all at once. This way it will not be so much like hard work and you will be able to have some gentle control over your habits on a day-to-day basis. There are many "healthy weight" people out there who cannot take their weight for granted and this tends to be the way they keep from gaining weight: by paying a little attention the whole time, rather than going on a massive "diet" and then trying to forget about the whole issue for a while.

Weight control does not have to be a huge effort. It work best when it is a little effort, but an effort made lightly and constantly.

How and When to Get Professional Help

At some point whilst you are trying to lose weight you may well think about getting some professional help. After all, that is what you would do with any other health problem.

In general, it is never a bad idea to consult a qualified professional. However, there are limits to what health professionals can do for you. Also, the government does not regulate some of the people that you might want to consult – such as counsellors or psychotherapists – so you need to take care about whom you consult. This section aims to let you know what your options are and to give you a realistic idea of what health professionals can – and can't – help with. We will deal with different types of help in turn.

Doctors

In general, there are two types of doctor that you could see about weight problems. First, there is your family doctor. Second, they may refer you to a specialist. There are very few specialists in weight management in the UK, so we will focus on what your family doctor can do for you.

In general, your family doctor can do four things for you. They can check that your weight problem does not have a medical cause and they can refer you to another professional, in particular to a dietician (*see below*). They may also be able to prescribe medication to help with your weight loss (*again, more below*), or refer you to an exercise scheme at a local gym (a good idea, if it suits you).

It is always wise to have any serious long-term weight problem checked out medically. Sometimes there are medical conditions, such as hypothyroidism, that can cause weight problems and that can be treated. However, it is important to realize that the vast majority of people with weight problems do not have a medical condition underlying them. If your doctor checks you out and nothing is found that can account for your weight, then it is wise to accept this. It is unlikely that the doctor will have missed anything. Some people are convinced that they have a "hidden" problem even after being given the all-clear. This is unfortunate, as they could have focused on changing their habits instead. The cause of most people's weight problems is well known: the whole of our society has been eating more high-energy food and being less active.

There are two main weight-loss treatments that doctors can arrange: medication and surgery. Surgery is only available in very specialist clinics. Medication is more common.

Medication for weight loss
Your family doctor may be willing to prescribe medication for weight loss. Also, you can buy "weight-loss" medication and supplements from commercial sources, for example over the internet. We will deal with these commercial drugs first.

There are a staggering number of different weight-loss pills and supplements on the market. There are three solid facts about nearly all of them that you need to know:

1. There is absolutely no evidence that they will help you lose weight in anything but the very short term.

2. They will cost you money.
3. There are side-effects associated with all of them.

We have seen many people who have been affected in the long term – often psychologically – by these substances. And many people make a lot of money by selling useless "cures" to people who are desperate to lose weight. Our advice is to steer clear of these damaging scams.

However, there is better news for prescription drugs. There are two types of weight-loss drug and they can work well for a while and can be administered safely by your doctor. The first type makes you feel "full" sooner. The second type affects how food is broken down in your stomach, making sure that you absorb less fat. Both of these types have been well tested and can help with weight loss. There are, however, side-effects associated with their use and generally they only work for as long as you take them. Of course, in the long term they will not work for you unless you make sure that you take charge of your eating whilst you are taking them. For example, imagine that you took one of these drugs and lost weight for six months, but you did not really change your habits in that time. What would happen when you stopped taking them?

Sometime prescription drugs can also help with this, though. For example, eating fatty food whilst taking the drug that affects fat breakdown can result in some mildly unpleasant effects – it teaches you which foods are high-fat pretty fast. However, it is important not to overestimate how much they can help in the long term. It is easy to have high hopes for these drugs – a person might say, "If I just get a bit of help from the drugs, I can change my habits." Of course, this can happen, and it is great when it does. However, many people do not follow through on their big promises. The promises were a way of avoiding the issue.

If it is worth changing your habits, then it is worth starting it now. Avoiding it or saying that you will do it when you get some drugs will get you nowhere. No medication can change your habits for you.

Surgery

Surgery is a drastic approach to weight loss, but one that is becoming increasingly used as more people become severely overweight. Essentially, it involves changing a person's gut. One type of surgery makes the stomach smaller, making it impossible to eat large amounts. The other type "bypasses" some sections of gut so that food is not absorbed into the body so well.

Both types of surgery result in impressive levels of weight loss. People usually lose a lot of weight quite fast and their risk of medical problems related to their weight goes down. However, there are lots of side-effects associated with both forms of surgery. First, this is major surgery, which is a risky business. Second, although a person will usually be lighter after surgery and their risk of medical complications will be lower, life will not be simple. There are lots of unpleasant side-effects, such as vomiting and malnutrition, which are serious issues. Surgery can sound great for someone who dreams of going to a party with a new slim body and nice clothes. However, it is quite possible that the full picture would also involve having to run to the toilet to vomit after eating a bit too much from the buffet. It is wise to be realistic.

Where people are very severely overweight, surgery can save lives. However, it is a long way from being a "magic cure". Also, anyone can "beat" the surgery. Bad eating habits will always defeat it. For example, even if you have a very small stomach, liquids like soft cheese or full-sugar fizzy drinks can pass right through. Even with surgery, there is no escape from having to look at your eating and activity habits.

Dieticians

As medical and surgical options are complicated and will never change your habits for you, instead you may decide to get as much help as possible to "go it alone". In this situation, a dietician can be a great option. Dieticians are experts on food and nutrition, and are well-trained health professionals. If you are trying to lose weight, it is never a bad idea to consult a dietician.

As well as educating you about the food you eat, a dietician can help you to make useful plans to change your habits. A huge part of their job is showing people how to change their eating for the better, so there is a very good chance that they will have some useful ideas for you! Also, remember that food is about more than just weight. A dietician can advise you on the types of food that will make you most healthy in the long term, or about the foods that will give you the most energy (*see also Chapter 5*).

Dieticians can also provide regular checking and monitoring to help you keep on track. However, you will need to be honest with your dietician and ultimately, as always, habit change has to come from you.

Getting Help for Emotional Problems

Emotional problems can be a serious block to weight loss. If you find they are quite serious, it is a good idea to try to get some professional help with them.

There are two routes here: first, to get help through your doctor, and second, to seek counselling or psychotherapy privately or from a voluntary organization.

Your family doctor is your first point of contact for all health problems, including problems with your emotional health. They can arrange two types of treatment for you: psychological therapy or medication. You will probably be offered medication first, because it is simpler, cheaper (let's be honest) and it can be started immediately. Unfortunately, waiting lists for psychological therapy are usually very long. However, medication is not the best option for everybody, so don't be afraid to be assertive with your doctor and clearly state your desire for psychological help if you feel you need it.

If your doctor refers you for psychological help, this should be with a qualified practitioner. However, you should still have a look at the ideas for checking out your therapist below.

On the other hand, if you are offered medication, such as antidepressants, there are a few things that it is useful to know.

How to Do It

Medication for emotional difficulties

Medication can be an incredibly useful treatment for emotional difficulties. However, many people do not like the idea of taking pills to help their mood. People often say that pills "don't really solve the problem". This is partly true – and partly untrue. If the "problem" is really long periods of sadness and crying, then pills sometimes will "solve" it. However, it is more usual that pills give people the strength and energy *to solve their problems themselves*. It is hard to solve problems when you can hardly think because you are worrying all the time. Medication can give you the freedom to help yourself.

There are some other worries about medication. First, people worry that it is "addictive". Second, others worry that it "covers up the problem" but doesn't deal with it. Both of these are mainly untrue. Modern forms of medication are usually not like the older drugs such as Valium (diazepam) that can cause dependence. They are usually a completely different type of chemical and do not cause people to become dependent in the same way. Even if your doctor does prescribe a Valium-type drug, you will not be given it for long enough to become dependent on it. However, it is true that occasionally people have difficulties in coming off modern drugs. These difficulties are not common and can usually be managed with a little help from your doctor. As for "covering up the problem", as we noted above, pills will often give you the strength to solve problems yourself. However, they cannot mend broken relationships or enable you to come to terms with really difficult life circumstances. You will have to do this work yourself.

There are a couple of basic facts about medication. First, it does not work for everyone. Second, it often has side-effects. Unfortunately, there is sometimes a period when starting new medication during which you *get side-effects but do not get any benefits*. This means it is important to stick with any drug for a few weeks before deciding it is not working.

The key to getting the most out of medication is to listen hard to your doctor, ask lots of questions and follow their advice. Then, when you have done all of this, to be really honest about whether the drug is working for you. Finally, be honest to your doctor about this too!

Psychological help – psychotherapy and counselling

The alternative to medication is psychological help. The trouble with this is that there are almost as many types of therapy as there are drugs! Also, there are many different types of people out there giving therapy. There are mental health professionals – for example, clinical psychologists, who have extensive training in psychological therapy. Also, some psychiatrists and psychiatric nurses have some training in therapy. More commonly, there are people who are not mental health professionals but who have specific training in counselling and psychotherapy. It can be very hard for someone who does not know about all of this to understand which type of therapy to opt for and which "therapists" to trust. We cannot give a complete guide here, but we will cover three different topics: types of therapy, the qualifications of therapists and most importantly, how to spot a decent therapist.

There are lots of different types of therapy and counselling out there. We know that some are helpful, because scientific studies have shown this. For example, CBT – cognitive-behavioral therapy – is a useful type of therapy for many (but certainly not all) people. However, there is a big secret in the therapy world that many people hate to admit to – most types of psychological therapy have *never been properly tested to see if they work*. Also, many therapies aim at dealing with emotions rather than doing the kind of practical habit change you need to lose weight. So you need to be clear about what you want and then be a little careful.

We would suggest that you opt for CBT if you can get it, and if you can't get it, then pick someone with good qualifications whom you feel that you can trust. The details of the main CBT organization in the UK, the BABCP, and the ABCT in the US, are in Appendix II. There is more on spotting a decent therapist below. Other than this, we can only offer one piece of advice: if you have the choice between short-term therapy (this usually means up to 20 sessions!) and long-term therapy, it is smart to choose short-term first. Good short-term therapies can be very effective and there is no point using a sledge-hammer to crack a nut. If a person strongly recommends that you try long-term therapy before you have even had a go at something shorter, be cautious and ask them why.

Also, use a qualified therapist. If a person is a mental health professional (for example a clinical or counselling psychologist, psychiatrist, nurse or social worker) then they should have some idea what they are talking about. However, it is still a very good idea to use the tips on spotting a reliable therapist below. With counsellors and psychotherapists, check that they are accredited by some kind of professional body and that they get regular supervision. The details of professional bodies such as the British Psychological Society are in Appendix II.

Finally, trust your feelings about your therapist. If you meet them for the first time and they seem competent, easy to talk to and open, this is a good sign. If it doesn't feel right, you may still decide to give it a go, but don't be afraid to "shop around". Below is a list of questions that you can ask any therapist. Check their reactions and see how convincing you find them:

- What are your qualifications?
- Which professional body do you belong to?
- Which code of ethics do you follow?
- Do you have a qualified supervisor to discuss your work with?
- Is there a complaints procedure?
- For how many years have you been practising?
- How long is a session?
- How often are sessions held?
- What do you charge?
- Is there a cancellation fee?
- Is it a totally confidential service? (Be suspicious if they say "yes" – would they really not tell anyone if you were obviously a risk to your own – or someone else's – health?)

- When might confidentiality be broken?
- How long might the therapy last for?
- How does therapy end?

These questions were put together by POPAN – the Prevention of Professional Abuse Network (*details in Appendix II*) (though the note in brackets is our own). POPAN also has some good advice on warning signs that things might not be going well with your therapist – have a look at their website or phone them if you are concerned.

These guidelines are just general advice – the overall idea is to give a therapist enough time to prove themselves and then if you are not convinced, tell them why. If they cannot deal with your concerns and answer your questions, change therapist. This may all sound a bit negative, and it is certainly true that many people have benefited greatly from a private therapist. However, is still true that in the UK the government spends more effort regulating the people who service your car than the people you trust to give you therapy. So caution is sensible.

Some Parting Words

This is the end of this book. We wish you every success with losing weight – and keeping it off. Remember, the right approach is to focus on changing habits. This is not easy, and there is no guarantee that you will succeed. However, no one else can guarantee weight loss either. Don't trust anyone who says they can!

Professionals and semi-professionals might be able to help you with weight loss. However, even if they do, the effort will all have come from you, and you should take all the credit! People's weight problems are never "fixed" by others (or at least only temporarily). You will always need to find the way for yourself.

Please do not underestimate yourself, no matter what your history with weight loss. Do not make too many assumptions about what you can and cannot do. Each new time you try to change, you are a different person from the last time – you have different experiences and memories. Each time is different. Remember, there are people out there who have failed on 20 diets, but succeeded on their 21st attempt to lose weight.

We encourage you to use the ideas in this book as tools – tools that you can use to create your own individual success. Also, be prepared to do your own thinking and use all of your active, intelligent ways of coping with situations. Good luck!

Appendix I
Planning and Recording

Body Mass Index

	5'0"	5'1"	5'2"	5'3"	5'4"	5'5"	5'6"	5'7"	5'8"	5'9"	5'10"	5'11"	6'0"	6'1"	6'2"	6'3"	6'4"
9st	25	24	23	22	22	21	20	20	19	19	18	18	17	17	16	16	15
9.5st	26	25	24	24	23	22	21	21	20	20	19	19	18	18	17	17	16
10st	27	26	26	25	24	23	23	22	21	21	20	20	19	18	18	17	17
10.5st	29	28	27	26	25	24	24	23	22	22	21	21	20	19	19	18	18
11st	30	29	28	27	26	26	25	24	23	23	22	21	21	20	20	19	19
11.5st	31	30	29	29	28	27	26	25	24	24	23	22	22	21	21	20	20
12st	33	32	31	30	29	28	27	26	26	25	24	23	23	22	22	21	20
12.5st	34	33	32	31	30	29	28	27	27	26	25	24	24	23	22	22	21
13st	36	34	33	32	31	30	29	29	28	27	26	25	25	24	23	23	22
13.5st	37	36	35	33	32	31	31	30	29	28	27	26	26	25	24	24	23
14st	38	37	36	35	34	33	32	31	30	29	28	27	27	26	25	24	24
14.5st	40	38	37	36	35	34	33	32	31	30	29	28	28	27	26	25	25
15st	41	40	38	37	36	35	34	33	32	31	30	29	28	28	27	26	26
15.5st	42	41	40	38	37	36	35	34	33	32	31	30	29	29	28	27	26
16st	44	42	41	40	38	37	36	35	34	33	32	31	30	30	29	28	27
16.5st	45	44	42	41	40	38	37	36	35	34	33	32	31	30	30	29	28
17st	46	45	44	42	41	40	38	37	36	35	34	33	32	31	31	30	29
17.5st	48	46	45	43	42	41	40	38	37	36	35	34	33	32	31	31	30
18st	49	48	46	45	43	42	41	39	38	37	36	35	34	33	32	31	31
18.5st	51	49	47	46	44	43	42	41	39	38	37	36	35	34	33	32	32
19st	52	50	49	47	46	44	43	42	40	39	38	37	36	35	34	33	32
19.5st	53	52	50	48	47	45	44	43	42	40	39	38	37	36	35	34	33
20st	55	53	51	50	48	47	45	44	43	41	40	39	38	37	36	35	34
20.5st	56	54	52	51	49	48	46	45	44	42	41	40	39	38	37	36	35
21st	57	56	54	52	50	49	47	46	45	43	42	41	40	39	38	37	36
21.5st	59	57	55	53	52	50	49	47	46	44	43	42	41	40	39	38	37
22st	60	58	56	55	53	51	50	48	47	45	44	43	42	41	40	38	37

Calculate your BMI by finding your weight (in stones) on the left and then your height (in feet and inches) above. The number that you read off from the table is your BMI.

Questioning and Expanding your Thinking

Summary of the process

You will need a pen and paper. Here's the whole process. It is not complicated – it boils down to working out what is bothering you, and then checking out your view of the situation. Remember to refer back to Chapter 2 to remind yourself about the full details of this process.

1. Pinpoint the thought.
   Explain the thought fully.
   Summarize the most upsetting or difficult part.
2. Question it.
   Use the questions below.
3. Expand your thinking.
   Find three alternative views of the situation.

Long list of questions

Below is a list of ten questions that can usefully be applied to almost any thought. Use this "long" list when you are starting to use this process. It is also useful for very difficult or "stuck" thoughts. Of course, not all questions will apply to the particular thought that you are dealing with.

1. What is the evidence for this thought? What is the evidence against it?
2. What are other ways of thinking about this situation?
3. How would another person see this situation? What would I say to my best friend or someone I loved if they were in the same situation?
4. What are the advantages and disadvantages of thinking this way?
5. When I am not feeling this way, do I think about this type of situation differently? How?
6. Am I asking questions that have no answers?

7. Five years from now, if I look back at this situation, will I look at it any differently? Will I pay attention to other parts of the situation that I'm ignoring now?
8. Are there any small things that show my thoughts aren't true? Am I ignoring them or not taking them seriously?
9. Am I blaming myself for something over which I do not have complete control? Am I forgetting that other people are responsible for their own behaviour (and I'm not responsible for what they do)?
10. Am I always thinking that things will go badly? Am I exaggerating how bad things would be if they did go wrong?

Short list of questions

When you have had some practice in questioning and expanding thoughts with the long list, you may find that you just need to use the questions below. If you find a particularly difficult thought, then go back to the long list.

- Is this thought *true* (and unbiased)?
- Is this thought *helpful*?
- What are *other ways* of looking at the situation?

Activity Record Form

Time	Situation	Moods or sensations	Activity
06.00			
07.00			
08.00			
09.00			
10.00			
11.00			
12.00			
13.00			
14.00			
15.00			
16.00			
17.00			
18.00			
19.00			
20.00			
21.00			
22.00			
23.00			
24.00			
01.00			

Important automatic thoughts:

Pedometer reading:

Eating Record Form

Situation and time	Mood or sensation	Eating

Important automatic thoughts:	

Planning Forms

Activity/exercise plans

- What exactly is the plan? (Amounts Count!)

- What help do you need for your plan? Whose support would be helpful?

- When are you going to start, and when are you going to check and review your plan?

Eating/food plans

- What exactly is the plan? (Amounts Count!)

- What help do you need for your plan? Whose support would be helpful?

- When are you going to start, and when are you going to check and review your plan?

Reasons

- What are the good reasons for spending time and effort making these plans work?

Problem-Solving

Problem-solving is an absolutely critical part of losing weight and keeping it off. Practise these techniques and use them a lot! Remember that actually going through the steps with pen and paper is the only way to do it. If you try to "just think the problem through", you may be successful, but you will more often be disappointed. Use the technique fully.

A *quick summary of the process*

These are the basic steps of problem-solving.

1. Define your problem.
2. Make up lots of alternative solutions.
3. Analyse your alternatives.
4. Try out your solution(s).
5. See how it went – and do it again!

Below are some helpful tips for each stage of the process:

Define your problem

- What exactly is the problem? Try to be really clear.
- Are you sure that this is your problem? Check that you are working on the right issue.
- Are you trying to solve a huge problem? Try to break it down into smaller ones and work on one of these.

Make up lots of alternative solutions

- Remember that anything goes. Do not criticize or reject any ideas at this stage.
- Start off with some silly ideas if you get stuck. They help to get things going.
- Keep going until you have plenty of alternatives. Make sure you have at least five, preferably ten!

Analyse your alternatives

- Throw out the options that really will not work.
- Work out how good the other options would be in the short, medium and long term.
- Always remember that you are trying to build positive habits that will stay with you.

Try out your solution(s)

- Make your solution a SMART solution (*see Chapter 6*).
- Make sure that you really try your solution out in real life. This is where you will learn most.

See how it went – and do it again!

- Be honest about how well it worked.
- Do not be critical if your solution only produced a small change. A small genuine change is better than a big change that will not last.
- If your solution did not work, this is not a "failure". Instead it means that you have just learned something important. Learning what does not work is central to the process.
- Problem-solving is a repeated process of being flexible and creative. Keep going and try it again!

Appendix II
Taking It Further

Useful Organizations

Professional

These organizations represent particular professions. They usually hold information about their own profession and have lists of registered professionals/therapists. Often they are the place to go if you wish to register a complaint or disciplinary issue.

The British Dietetic Association (BDA)
Professional organization for dieticians. Lists of registered dieticians, information.
Tel: 0121 200 8080
Web: www.bda.uk.com
email: info@bda.uk.com

The British Psychological Society (BPS)
Professional organization for psychologists, including clinical psychologists, counselling psychologists and health psychologists.
Tel: 0116 254 9568
Web: www.bps.org.uk
email: enquiry@bps.org.uk

The General Medical Council (GMC)
National body that registers doctors and organizes complaints and disciplinary procedures.
Tel: 0845 3573 456
Web: www.gmc-uk.org
email: gmc@gmc-uk.org

The Health Care Commission
The body regulating the quality of NHS and private health care.
Tel: 020 7448 9200
Web: www.healthcarecommission.org.uk
email: feedback@healthcarecommission.org.uk

US Organizations

Association for Behavioral and Cognitive Therapies
Cognitive Therapies (ABCT, formerly AABT)
Clinical Directory and Referral Service.
Tel: (00 1) 212 647 1890
Web: www.aabt.org

National Institute of Mental Health (NIMH)
Working to Improve Mental Health.
Tel: (00 1) 301 443 4513
Web: www.nimh.nih.gov
email: nimhinfo@nih.gov

Therapy

These organizations represent people practising a particular type
of psychological therapy. They ensure a certain level of training
and a code of conduct. However, the people involved need not
have had any training as a health care professional (for example,
a person may have originally been an accountant, teacher or
butcher and then become a counsellor or psychotherapist).
The exception is the BABCP (immediately below), which
does require professional qualification in a "core profession"
(e.g. psychology, nursing, social work) to be accredited as a
CBT therapist.

The British Association for Behavioural and Cognitive Psychotherapies (BABCP)
Professional organization for CBT therapists. Provides information and a list of trained therapists.
Tel: 01254 875 277
Web: www.babcp.com
email: babcp@babcp.com

The British Association for Counselling and Psychotherapy (BACP)
Lists of UK counsellors and psychotherapists.
Tel: 0870 443 5252
Web: www.counselling.org.uk

The British Confederation of Psychotherapists (BCP)
Organization for people practising more long-term psychotherapy/psychoanalytical treatments.
Tel: 020 7267 3626
Web: www.bcp.org.uk
email: mail@bcp.org.uk

The UK Council of Psychotherapy (UKCP)
Information about psychotherapy. Holds its own register of psychotherapists.
Tel: 020 7436 3002
Web: www.psychotherapy.org.uk
email: ukcp@psychotherapy.org.uk

Voluntary/Self-Help

Depression Alliance
Information on depression and support.
Tel: 0845 123 23 20
Web: www.depressionalliance.org

Eating Disorders Alliance (EDA)
Information on bulimia, anorexia, binge eating.
Tel: 0870 770 3221
Web: www.edauk.com
email: media@edauk.com

MIND
National association for mental health. Information, advice
and advocacy.
Tel: 0845 766 1063
Web: www.mind.org.uk
email: contact@mind.org.uk

Prevention of Professional Abuse Network (POPAN)
Organization devoted to stopping professionals mistreating
people under their care. Useful if you are concerned about how
a professional is treating you.
Tel: 0845 4500 300
Web: www.popan.org.uk
email: info@popan.org.uk

Weight Concern
Group devoted to the physical and psychological well-being of
overweight people.
Tel: 020 7679 6636
Web: www.weightconcern.com
email: enquiries@weightconcern.com

*Are services for overweight people in
your area inadequate?*

Services across the UK are inadequate. If you feel strongly
about this, you can contact your MP and let them know how
you feel. You can find out your MP's details on:
Web: www.locata.co.uk/commons/

Useful Websites

These websites contain useful information about weight and its health consequences.

www.bdaweightwise.com
Very useful website from the British Dietetic Association that covers all aspects of being overweight and weight loss.

www.weightconcern.com
Weight Concern charity, as listed in "Organizations" above. Contains good material on weight, health risks and nutrition and exercise.

www.nutrition.org.uk
British Nutrition Foundation. Aims to provide scientifically sound information about nutrition.

www.nhsdirect.nhs.uk
NHS Direct website. Comprehensive information about NHS services and self-help information on common conditions.

www.shapeup.org
American not-for-profit organization providing information on healthy weight.

www.bospa.org.uk
British Obesity Surgery Patient Association. Provides information for people thinking about surgery for weight problems.

http://www.publications.parliament.uk/pa/cm200304/cmselect/cmhealth/23/23.pdf
The House of Commons Health Committee Report on Obesity in the UK, published in 2004. A comprehensive look at obesity in the UK – causes, consequences and NHS services. A large, well-researched – and sometimes angry – document.

For professionals and campaigners

www.aso.org.uk
The Association for the Study of Obesity. Mainly for researchers and professionals. Contains a useful "information centre" with fact sheets.

www.domuk.org
Dieticians working in Obesity Management UK. For dieticians with a specialist interest in obesity management.

www.nationalobesityforum.org.uk
Mainly for professionals. Reviews of literature, developments in services.

www.obesity.org
American Obesity Association. American campaigning group.

Useful Reading

Binge-eating and bulimia

Cooper, Peter J., *Bulimia Nervosa and Binge Eating*, London: Constable & Robinson, 1993; Quality self-help book.

Fairburn, Christopher, *Overcoming Binge Eating*, New York: Guilford Press, 1995; Very clear and practical.

Schmidt, Ulrike, and Treasure, Janet, *Getting Better Bit(e) by Bit(e): A Survival Kit for Sufferers of Bulimia Nervosa and Binge Eating Disorders*, Hove, UK: Psychology Press, 1993; Good, wide-ranging book including chapters on being assertive and dealing with a history of abuse.

Cognitive Behavioral Therapy

Burns, David D., *Feeling Good: The New Mood Therapy*, New York: Avon Books, 1980; Large book containing a wide range of material, from managing depression to relationships.

Greenberger, Dennis, and Padesky, Christine, *Mind over Mood: Changing the Way You Feel by Changing the Way You Think*, New York: Guilford Press, 1995; Practical, lots of monitoring sheets, examples, handouts, etc; very good for developing CBT skills.

Depression and general low self-regard

Fennell, Melanie, *Overcoming Low Self-Esteem*, London: Constable & Robinson, 1999; Strongly recommended for those whose poor self-esteem is a long-standing problem.

Gilbert, Paul, *Overcoming Depression*, London: Constable & Robinson, 2000; Excellent – detailed, practical, with case studies.

Low-fat diets

The American Dietetic Association, *Cut the Fat*, New York: HarperCollins*Publishers*, 1999.

American Heart Association Low-Fat Low-Cholesterol Cookbook: Heart-Healthy Easy-to-Make Recipes That Taste Great, New York: Clarkson N. Potter Publishers, 2001.

Coleman, Mary, *Healthy Eating: Low Fat*, Sydney: The Australian Women's Weekly Home Library, 2000.

Relationship difficulties and communication skills

Alberti, Robert E., and Emmons, Michael L., *Your Perfect Right: Guide to Assertive Living*, Atascadero, California: Impact Publishers, 1996; Classic American text on assertiveness.

Beck, Aaron T., *Love is Never Enough: How Couples Can Overcome Misunderstandings, Resolve Conflicts, and Solve Relationship Problems through Cognitive Therapy*, New York: HarperCollins*Publishers*, 1988; CBT approach to relationship problems – pragmatic, sensible.

Stone, Douglas, Patton, Bruce, and Heen, Sheila, *Difficult Conversations: How to Discuss What Matters Most*, London: Michael Joseph, 1999; Excellent book from the management/ business literature on handling conflict and difficult conversations.

Index

Index

Order further books in the *Overcoming* series

No. of copies	Title	Price	Total
	Anger and Irritability	£7.99	
	Anorexia Nervosa	£7.99	
	Anxiety	£7.99	
	Bulimia Nervosa and Binge-Eating	£7.99	
	Childhood Trauma	£7.99	
	Chronic Fatigue	£9.99	
	Depression	£7.99	
	Low Self-Esteem	£7.99	
	Mood Swings	£7.99	
	Obsessive Compulsive Disorder	£7.99	
	Panic	£7.99	
	Relationship Problems	£9.99	
	Sexual Problems	£9.99	
	Social Anxiety and Shyness	£7.99	
	Traumatic Stress	£7.99	
	Your Smoking Habit	£9.99	
	P&P & Insurance		£2.50
	Grand Total		£

Name. _____

Address: _____

_____ Postcode: _____

Daytime Tel. No. / Email _____
(in case of query)

Three ways to pay:

1. **For express service telephone the TBS order line on 01206 255 800 and quote 'CRBK1'. Order lines are open Monday–Friday 8:30a.m. – 5:30p.m.**

2. I enclose a cheque made payable to **TBS Ltd** for £_____

3. Please charge my ❏ Visa ❏ Mastercard ❏ Amex ❏ Switch (switch issue no. ....) £_____

   Card number: _____

   Expiry date: _____ Signature _____

   (your signature is essential when paying by credit card)

Please return forms (*no stamp required*) to, Constable & Robinson Ltd, FREEPOST NAT6619, 3 The Lanchesters, 162 Fulham Palace Road, London W6 9BR. All books subject to availability.

Enquiries to readers@constablerobinson.com
www.constablerobinson.com

Constable & Robinson Ltd (directly or via its agents) may mail or phone you about promotions or products. Tick box if you do not want these from us ❏ or our subsidiaries.